THE OCEAN

THE OCEAN

MAN'S CONQUEST OF THE SEA

by Alan Villiers

ILLUSTRATED

E. P. DUTTON & CO., INC. • NEW YORK

PREFACE

MY PURPOSE IN THIS BOOK IS TO INTRODUCE SOME ASPECTS of the widely varied and always interesting story of the ocean and to stimulate interest in the sea "and all that therein is." I have given some account of the ocean itself, of man's struggle with it, which is still going on, and of the development of his ships.

In doing this, I am aware of the shelves of excellent works already published, and I make no pretense to any specialized knowledge.

What I have drawn on, whenever I could, is my own personal experience of the sea. After all, the engineless, ocean-going sailing ship, large or small, was probably the ideal observation post for the study of the deep sea and at least some of its surface and near-the-surface creatures. We were often at sea in such ships continuously for over one hundred days, once for over one hundred and fifty.

I have tried to diversify my sailing experience, too. I have sailed my own square-trigger—a full-rigged ship—around the world, not hurrying. I spent a year with the Arabs in their Red Sea and Indian Ocean dhows. I have sailed with the Maldivians, the Trobriand Islanders, and the pearlers of the Persian Gulf. I was a working member in the whaling factory-ship *Sir James Clark Ross* of the pioneer pelagic whaling expedition into the Ross Sea in 1923–1924. I have made two voyages to the fishing banks off Newfoundland and Greenland, one of

5

six months in the Portuguese dory-fishing schooner *Argus* in 1950, the other some years later in the Portuguese four-thousand-ton hospital-and-assistance ship *Gil Eannes*. I have commanded two reconstructed eighteenth-century frigates in the Mediterranean and delivered the replica of a late sixteenth-century bark across the North Atlantic, from England to America.

In 1962, for a change, I was invited to sail with the nuclear ship *Savannah*, when she made history by being the first cargo and passenger-carrying merchantman to go to sea under nuclear power.

All this was valuable experience, some of it unique. I have drawn upon whatever has seemed relevant in preparing this book, to give, here and there perhaps, some better point to the story.

I have also had the good fortune to write the book at sea, aboard the Blue Funnel Line's S.S. *Helenus* on passage from Australia, via Suez, to France and England, among seamen of today.

ALAN VILLIERS

S.S. *Helenus*
December 1962

CONTENTS

Chapter 1 • **ONE OCEAN**

IF ALL THE LAND THERE IS, EVERY CONTINENT AND EVERY island, were sliced off at present sea level and bulldozed under water, the world would still be covered by an ocean two miles deep. There is fifteen times more water in the sea than the entire volume of all the exposed land. Sea covers 70 percent of the globe—139 million square miles of it. The sea at its deepest—in the Marianas Trench of the Pacific Ocean—is more than a mile deeper than the highest mountain. The sea's average depth is over five times the average height of the land. In one cubic mile of the sea there are 166 million tons of salts. If all the salt of the sea were suddenly precipitated over all the land, it would cover the lot to a height of five hundred feet.

Life on earth, say the scientists, began in the sea, which for millions of years was a kinder environment than the harsh and sterile cooling rocks of what became the land. Man himself was cradled in the sea. He emerged a protoplasm, returned a fisherman and a mariner. To this day his body is three parts water—he cannot sustain life without salt or water.

From the minute plants of the phytoplankton adrift in the sunlit surface of the sea to the astonishing denizens of its pressurized, dark, and abysmal depths, the sea sustains as varied, interesting, and important a range of life as the land. The sea is the last great source of food for man; it is still awaiting intensive exploitation.

The life of the sea has an immense, almost an infinite

9

Alan Villiers

Big Sea—little ship

fecundity. A single oyster has nearly 2 million eggs at a spawning, and the humble codfish betters this by two and often three times. If all the cod spawn lived, the ocean would be filled with cod just as the New York subway is jammed with people in the rush hours. As with the oyster and the cod, so also with the rest of the amazingly abundant sea life. Millions, billions, quadrillions die; yet the permanent population of the sea, consisting of the minute fraction which struggles to maturity, remains a varied and prolific immensity which oceanographers are only now beginning to comprehend.

The sea gives life and takes life with an endless and tremendous abandon unequalled, indeed, unimaginable, anywhere on land. The surface waters of the sea, seen from below by a rising diver, abound with minute microscopic life which flits like sunbeams sprinkled liberally everywhere, too small to be seen except when the sunlight chances to fall on them. The blue whale, the largest animal ever known—it can exceed one hundred feet in length, weigh over one hundred tons—lives and flourishes in the ocean so long as it can avoid man's harpoon guns.

The astonishing, amazing sea has been there since time began—the great cleanser, the purifier, the climate-maker, weather-breeder, source of water and of life. For the sea to a great extent makes climate, with its onshore winds, its warmth-bringing, nutrient-filled currents, its vast movements of circulating waters both cold and hot.

Changes in the sea can and do affect great nations. The weather has been changing in recent years both in North America and in Europe. In the north in the 1960's arctic ice is melting at an extraordinary rate, uncovering land unseen for a thousand years. Glaciers are accelerating. Fish such as cod are found hundreds of miles north of their accustomed haunts. Sardines and tuna are in the North Sea. Ships pass between the Atlantic and Pacific by both the Northwest Passage around Alaska and the Northeast Passage around Siberia in numbers and at speeds hitherto unthinkable. Ports formerly ice-blocked half the year now stay open almost all year around. Hurricanes which used to be regarded as tropic storms now sweep up the eastern seaboard of the United States as far as Canada with tiresome and destructive regularity. The northern world is warming up; the last ice age recedes in its last fastnesses.

Why? Reasons are imperfectly known, but it seems certain that warmer oceanic air could be in large part the cause—changes in the wind blowing in from a warmer sea. For the sea winds pick up heat stored from the sun in the sea and radiated back again. In that part of the ocean called the North Atlantic there is a well-known movement of water known as the Gulf Stream, a drift of warmed water welling from the Gulf of Mexico, rushing up the Straits of Florida and along the American coast to Cape Hatteras at the rate of knots—three or four—then spreading and turning eastward and northeast to bring onshore winds that warm all northwest Europe. Because of this wide drift of warmed-up waters, the North Cape of Norway is ice-free the year around, while its counterpart in the same latitude across the North Atlantic—the north of Baffin Island—is locked all winter in impenetrable ice and cold.

The Gulf Stream changes, for reasons not now understood. Before the meteorologists really can make good weather forecasts on both sides of the North Atlantic, many oceanic mysteries must be probed.

The Gulf Stream is only one such ocean current. No sea is static: now a waste of waters tumbling in violent storms, now glassy in a stagnant calm with meaningless and utterly unpredictable rotation. The sea goes round and round, like a blood stream pumped by a mighty heart, and the heart is the heat of the sun. In the North Atlantic and the South Atlantic, both Pacifics, and the Indian Ocean, the story is much the same. Wind, sun, and the earth's rotation set up a surface water movement more or less well defined, reasonably reliable to seamen in the days of sail, and of great value in their voyaging—indeed, with the equally defined oceanic wind systems, the basis of it.

For no man could make long ocean voyages until first the ways of the ocean currents and winds were understood. As the currents are more or less constant, so are the great expanses of the tropic winds moving in from north and south toward the equator, deflected by the spin of the earth to northeast in the Northern Hemisphere and to southeast in the Southern Hemisphere.

Seamen still call these trade winds, for it was not until he understood them that man dared to essay real ocean voyages, as apart from coastal creeping along the land. Beyond the trade winds, to the north and south, are zones of changeable winds

and calms called variables. Beyond these again are the belts of
wild west winds with a west wind's drift of surface water whip-
ping along under them. Far enough north and south, at certain
seasons, easterlies blow.

So there is our ocean sea—not an indiscriminate mass of riotous waters for man's confusion and downfall, but a divinely
planned arrangement more or less orderly, though far from tidy;
a pattern, a *system* of winds and surface movements which
man had only to understand in order, in time, partially to tame
and bring to his use.

Now, in the 1960's, he has wide knowledge of the ocean's
surface behavior. But in real awareness of all its diverse qualities, in understanding its full potential for his use, he is still a
groper, an infant in an enormous library of fat, fact-filled books
which he has barely begun to learn how to read.

It is true that man feared the sea for untold centuries. For
the sea can and does provoke great storms to assault the land.
Mile upon mile of snarling breakers fling themselves endlessly
upon the shore with a force of two tons to the square foot.

The sea smashes, breaks through, destroys. The sea destroys
peninsulas, carves out islands, bars river mouths, washes away
old coastlines only to wash them up anew. The sea is both the
last and largest remaining source of food and the only possible
provision of fresh water in quantities sufficient for man's increasing, endless needs.

More than all this, the sea is a link and the great divider, a
highway and for centuries a barrier. And the sea is One—uni-
fied, world embracing. There is, in fact, one ocean—one ocean
with five great names and a thousand little ones. The Atlantic
flows into the Indian Ocean, the Pacific rushes to meet the
Atlantic around Cape Horn. There is no real boundary to any
sea save continental land. The waters mingle everywhere and
the names are geographic, for convenience only. The waters

of the Indian Ocean mingle with the Java Sea, China Sea, Yellow Sea, Southern Ocean, Arabian Sea, Red Sea, Persian Gulf, Bay of Bengal. The Caribbean, North, Arctic, Irish, Norwegian, and Baltic seas, the Gulf of St. Lawrence and the Gulf of Mexico, Hudson Bay and Denmark Strait are all sectors of the North Atlantic.

As for the Pacific, its named offshoots are legion. Seven Seas? There are more like seventy—all freely joined, open to one another somewhere or other, all accessible to the same ships except in places where the sea bottom reaches for the surface, its insufficient depth allowing it to float only the smallest vessels. The ice drifts freely across the sea at the top of the world in the far north, and a vast frozen continent keeps the free waters from the area of the South Pole.

In the Northern Hemisphere, the continent of North America stands squarely across the restless fetch of the ocean sea. In the south its waters may rush unchecked around the whole girdle of the globe, building up waves of an awesome, ferocious, and splendid height. Half a mile or more from crest to crest they run, tremendous, frightening, seen only by the wandering albatross, the whale, the Cape Horn seaman. Their dreadful, destructive grandeur is matched at times in the North Atlantic gales and in the mad storms called hurricanes— The ferocity of the screaming wind first holds the sea in frightened calm then, easing slightly in the greater wrath, rises in watery mountains which rush with a malign strength to bite at beaches, swamp estuaries, flatten islands, and fling ships large and small about like driftwood, in extremest peril despite their power and the strength man has built into them.

Man? Who is he to fight the sea, thinking he can use it? Himself largely water, a weak, upright creature ill balanced on the inefficient extremities of his two long legs, fearful of the sea which can drown him so easily, soak the life out of him, destroy him with a brief exposure. Yet man *has* fought back against the sea, with ingenuity and with heroism. He has sought not to tame it, for that is impossible, but to use it, to pit against it first his frail sailing craft, to probe and learn and, sometimes surviving, to bring back the knowledge so courageously gained to serve as a basis for discovering more.

Slowly, slowly, in one of the bravest and longest of all his stories, he has learned not quite yet to conquer the sea but to use it, to exploit it, to float on it his self-propelled, sea-going ships, which carry on his work upon this greatest of all highways. The sea is a God-given one-level freeway open to all peaceful nations, accessible from every sizable river, every inlet, every bay, every sound and gulf and anchorage around its countless thousands of miles of shore.

The seaworthy ships, once launched, manned, fueled, and laden, can go anywhere, for the sea has no frontiers, no customs barriers to pass. The continents offer roadways and railways but also marshes and mountain peaks, a babel of tongues, a confusion of governments all suspicious, man-made and man-obstructing boundaries and demarcations everywhere. The air can be flown through, at great expense, with speed but no other advantage, and the costliness and difficulty of this kind of transport preclude it, as yet, from the real bulk cargo movement essential to world trade.

Only the sea is a true highway, available always for the use of man.

It took him some time to learn to use it. It was one of the bravest and most adventurous forward steps he ever took. It was also one of the most important.

It is a story still far from ended. For the ocean has as yet yielded the least knowledge, given up the least of its secrets to the probing mind of man. The quest for knowledge and the story of achievement still roll on.

Chapter 2 • IN THE BEGINNING

THE SUN SHONE BRILLIANTLY IN THE GLORIOUSLY BLUE SKY and the water lapped softly along the golden sand, as if caressing its luxurious warmth. The sea breeze was coming in with just sufficient strength to provide a pleasant cooling air. To seaward, close offshore, a frail skimming dish of a craft was coming in under a wisp of sail. As I watched, the fisherman aboard, squatting at the stern, ran for a break in the reef, skipped through the break into the smooth water with the skill of a man who did it daily, ran up on the sand close by where I stood. Willing helpers from the small village beyond high water took his basket of fish, helped him haul the craft out of the sea.

Then, to my surprise, they began at once to take it to pieces, for it was nothing but a fragile raft of planks lashed together. The planks were roughly shaped like the blocks of a child's toy to fit in a crude sea shape and rise slightly in the bow and along the forepart on each side. A few simple lashings of rope made locally from the husks of coconuts held the planks in place. Mast and sail came down easily. There was no rudder, for a paddle sufficed to give the little raft direction—a paddle and the trim of the sail.

Within moments nothing but a few logs lay on the beach, drying. Other similar logs in groups of four and six lay about. I would not have realized what they were at all if I had not watched the fishing raft sail in and be dissembled.

16

Putting together a catamaran on the beach at Ceylon, near Jaffna

This was on a beach in the north of the island of Ceylon near Jaffna, three years ago. There are just as primitive craft elsewhere, doing a job of work at sea—plenty of them. Knocking about the world, I have seen a lot of them and sailed in several. I remembered a sailing raft similar to the Jaffna thing along the coast of Brazil just north of Recife. I was sailing that way one fine day with a full-rigged ship bound for Rio, and a fleet of these little things came skimming along. They called them *jangadas* there, and they had even less shape than those of the Singhalese. They were made of small logs of balsa.

It is amazing how many odd types of primitive craft survive, especially around the northern Indian Ocean. In the Persian Gulf I have seen fishing boats made of bundles of reeds lashed together in the form of a boat, with a fisherman sitting in them half awash. Along beaches in Ceylon, the South Seas, Arabia, New Guinea, and east Africa, I have seen men making dugout canoes and sailing them—sometimes twin-hulled with sheltered platforms built over them, more often with single or double outriggers to give beam enough to sit safely on the sea with their shallow draft. A dugout is a hollowed log. It could have no real stability without a stout outrigger.

Some of these dugouts have had remarkable features, for all their apparent simplicity. When European seamen first sailed into the Pacific they were astonished at the extent, variety, and voyages of the South Seas canoes. They found a population of some eight hundred thousand islanders, many of them well used to the sea, and spread over an area from eastward of Tahiti to New Zealand, from the Hawaiian Islands to the Carolines, over which they could have spread only by sea.

In the Marianas, north of Guam, the circumnavigating English admiral Anson was amazed at the speed and good sailing qualities of the native canoes. They flew along the top of the sea at three times the speed his lumbering big warship could make at her best—at 20 knots and more.

Looking closely, Anson observed a very curious thing. The hull shape was asymmetric, flat on one side, rounded on the other, providing a racing hull of scientific form and high efficiency which European naval architects could not equal until well into the twentieth century, if then.

What these canoes did was to pick up the wind and skim along on the surface of the water with the speed and grace of sea birds. The flat lee side offered *less* resistance as the wind pressed it down, and the canoe flew faster. Stability when necessary was maintained by agile seamen, laughing in the sun, who jumped out on the outrigger platform to windward as the canoe raced over the sunlit sea. Some of these canoes, Anson reported, were forty feet long.

Their simple lateen sail was shifted end-for-end when the vessel changed tacks, so that the flat side of the hull was always to leeward. For its purpose, which was voyaging among neighboring island groups such as the Marshalls and the Carolines, the hull was an ideal aerofoil.

Yet the natives knew nothing of aerodynamics. Neither does the Australian aborigine, developer of that other strange aerofoil, the returning boomerang. These people evolved the things they needed, whether swift canoe or bird-killing boomerang: having evolved them, they kept them and still (in the 1960's) use them. As they worked with and from nature, they used Nature's skill and grace: they evolved their know-how the simple way down countless thousands of years, as the sea birds did.

On the great rivers flowing into Asian seas strange craft still survive—inflated skins used to support either a swimming man or a light platform of cargo. Big round tubs of plaited weeds are used on the Euphrates in Iraq. I have seen boats with sewn hulls built up on a base of the two halves of a big dugout, split down the middle with some broad bottom planks secured between them, in use at Galle and near Nekombo, in Ceylon, and long rivercraft, like the canoes of the ancient Nile, fishing on the Brahmaputra in East Pakistan. Long, high-prowed, planked craft oddly like some Viking ships still work the huge lagoons of the atolls of the Maldive Islands. Fleets of round-bellied, primitive, one-masted square-rigged ships by the thousands carry the riverine commerce of East Pakistan. The junks of China, the shoe-shaped ships of Chittagong, a dozen types of sea-going and pearling dhow around the coasts of Arabia—I have seen these by the score, often by the hundreds, and sailed in some.

There were rivers which man could use thousands of years before there were any roads. Man could catch fish for his

Native canoes on the Kikori River in Papua, New Guinea

food in the shallow waters off sunlit bays with greater certainty and regularity than his primitive weapons and snares could take game. Floating logs offered easier transport than broad backs. They could be poled along or drift with the current. It was an easy step (though it probably took centuries) to think of shaping the logs, then hollowing them, to develop a paddle; to contrive a crude sail from matted leaves held up on a branch or, as the tens of centuries passed quietly by, to weave thick cloth, cut ropes from leather hides, plait coarse grass and creepers.

From all this to the sailing raft of lashed-together logs I saw near Jaffna was a simple, logical development. Having evolved, it stopped. From a thousand rivers and ten thousand beaches, canoes, rafts, reed craft braved the nearer seas in quest of food.

All this evolution was very likely confined to warm waters. Man might have come from the sea originally, but he very easily drowned in it and died swiftly of exposure. He was one of the poorest natural swimmers. Dogs, rats, even snakes could do better. His five-fingered hands and feet and the long slim limbs so useful on land were remarkably inefficient in the water, and his bare skin made him easily subject to exposure. He needed something to support himself and, if possible, to provide shelter.

Canoes, rafts, dugouts, inflated skins, and wicker baskets could float, but they would never be ships. They were shore-based, short-hop craft, of limited endurance, strictly for summer seas. Asian, Indian, and Arabian waters suited them in the good-weather seasons. Being sufficient for their purpose, they stayed and are still with us.

Sailing one evening quietly into the teeming city-port of Dacca on an arm of the Brahmaputra in East Pakistan, I reflected on these things. My vessel was a typical river trader, a long, fat graceful craft of oiled planks, brass-studded in geometric patterns especially around the low bow and built-out sternpost. One tall, slight mast held her gossamer sails to the soft evening wind. Long yards of bamboo divided deep course from huge square topsail—a primitive rig, primitively controlled, yet sufficient for its purpose. A round-roofed thatched house, built over the whole vessel from the small platform in the bow to a smaller aft, covered passengers, cargo, galley, and crew.

The breeze died; the sails ran down; the mast lay back in its simple tabernacle. Half the crew of thin, fit rivermen took poles, marched along an extremely narrow outboard platform built fore-and-aft along the ship, poling the heavy-laden hull along. They marched aft poling, back again with lifted sticks, with a rhythm and efficiency which had come down the centuries. The other half were rowing up for'ard, near the bows, three men on one side, three the other.

If I leaned outboard I could touch the river. A ripple would have swamped the little ship's low midships belly. Above the thatched house right aft, a bearded old river pilot, master of this craft, stood on a tiny platform built up there, just large enough to allow him to walk three paces. He grasped the long head of a sort of half-fixed, half-steering oar, half-rudder arrangement which looked as if it might have been developed from a Viking steering device of the year 800. By walking the little platform, now pushing now pulling its long handle, he contrived to use it with a slow sculling motion which both steered the vessel and added slightly to her forward way.

Around us were similar and slightly different rivercraft by the score. A long black canoe, easily seventy feet from raised stem to equally raised stern, was fishing with a huge net in the middle of the river, raising and lowering the net on two long wooden beams with a levering motion on a big tripod, like a huge wet scoop. I had seen similar scoop nets rigged ashore at the mouth of the Tiber at Fiumicino, near Rome.

And I had, I remembered, seen very similar vessels to some of these carved on temple walls in the valley of the Nile, in Egypt, and in reliefs at the Ashmolean, in Oxford, and other great museums.

This was in the year 1960.

Man went down to the sea long before he dared to cross it. Nor could he cross it ever, I thought, with riverine vessels such as the fleet on the Brahmaputra. When the rains came they must rush for shelter, lie up to wait for gentler weather. Such vessels served very well in a largely roadless, delta coun-try where each monsoon brought dreadful floods in which the headstrong Brahmaputra swelled to forty miles wide—un-bridged, untamable—and cut itself new beds as carelessly as a child draws a stick in wet sand.

But just beyond the river mouth, at Chittagong, where the ships must sail a little on the open Bay of Bengal, I noticed a very different class of vessel. Stronger hulled, more stoutly rigged, the sea-going Chittagong boats had a look of the Chi-nese junk.

I could understand man making trading voyages in such ships as these. I could see, too, how shore-based canoes could have survived involuntary voyages, driven offshore in a storm perhaps and unable to sail back again, or fleeing with their fishermen and families before some hungry, murdering in-vaders. Look at India, Malaya, Indonesia, the South Seas on the map; how easily island-group leads eastward to island-group, island to island the whole way, from the mouth of the Ganges-Brahmaputra river system down the coast of Burma, the Malay Archipelago, through all Indonesia, and close north by New Guinea to the Solomon Islands, with never more than a hundred miles of open sea to cross, and rarely that.

By this land-marked sea road the fleeing and the blown-away could and did reach the Pacific Ocean, driving always eastward until they came upon uninhabited islands and atoll groups where they could settle down.

For half the year the weather there was good, the winds sufficiently favorable. Wherever such primitive wanderers went (except when at last some reached New Zealand) they still sailed in tropic seas. Canoes were frail craft for such wandering but, sailed by the desperate, it was astonishing what voyages they could accomplish. Very obviously, such wanderers did sail to New Zealand, for their Polynesian descendants are still there. And from their Asian beginnings they had spread over almost every tropic island in the vast Pacific centuries before Europeans were competent or dared to sail that sea.

Asian waters bred true seamen pioneers who developed rivercraft well suited for their purpose. But with the canoe alone man could never conquer the open ocean or turn it to a highway for his trade.

For that he needed *ships*—large, staunch, seaworthy—able to make regular voyages to definite ports in a defined trade, and there sell and buy cargoes profitably, with assurance of peace and just government in wayside stops and turnaround ports from voyage beginning to voyage end. They had also to be able to navigate, to have clear knowledge of the ports to which they sailed and of how to find the path both there and back again over the trackless sea.

In tropical Asian waters all this had been evolved, too, long before the time of Christ; some of it survived until very recently.

Chapter 3 • **I LEARN FOR MYSELF**

I STOOD ON THE BEACH AT A PLACE CALLED MA'ALLA ON THE harbor at Aden in South Arabia and watched the fascinating sight of Arab and Somali commerce being conducted before my eyes. Close by, off Steamer Point, a dozen big liners and cargo ships from Europe bustled with their rattling winches and hordes of motor launches taking the passengers ashore, great sleek ships with tier upon tier of decks rising above enormous steel hulls, or deeply laden cargo vessels potbellied and low in the water with the produce of Asia which they were hurrying to Europe.

But at Ma'alla there was a fleet of dhows—nothing to do with the modern ships, nothing to do with the twentieth century, not an engine among them nor a winch, nor as much as a real lifeboat in the lot. Close in, propped up on the beach, were some big fellows of several hundred tons, their masts rigged down and their holds empty. Hordes of singing Arab seamen in long gowns that flapped in the breeze were slapping hot tallow on the undersides with their hands. Smaller dhows lay at anchor with rope cables such as European ships had used centuries earlier. Dugout canoes were paddled here and there with sailors joining their ships, and sometimes a captain.

From one of the big dhows farther out an oiled longboat was pulling in, two dozen chesty mariners pulling at her lashed-up oars with style and rhythm and a serang on his haunches beating time on a skin drum. Standing aft was a figure like a sheik of the Arabian desert, a lithe, tall, dark mustached man

25

Dhow in the Persian Gulf

of handsome and imperious countenance, his clothing a white linen robe reaching to his ankles and, over this, a gown flung loosely which was the color of pale gold and secured with tassles of gold wire. On his head was a gold-and-white head-cloth such as desert Arabs wear, bound in place by a double piece of pure white lamb's wool twisted into a soft rope and bound together at regular intervals with more gold wire.

Altogether the effect was striking; here obviously was a prince among the dhow captains, an Indian Ocean wanderer descended from a long, long line of sailing merchant sea captains, master of a ship of importance, probably belonging to the Sheik of Kuwait.

I looked carefully at this ship he'd come from. She was a big oiled beauty with two high masts, a double-ender (sharp at both ends) with an enormous stempost built out before her, a high poop, and altogether a look as if she had just sailed out of the tenth century and, once outside this modern port, was going back there.

The year was 1938. I had good reason to examine this big dhow with care, for I had arranged to sail with her wherever she might go. She was already laden and would sail that evening. I would be alone with her crew of thirty. Her movements were vague. Days, dates, even the year meant nothing to her or to those who had used her for their ancient commerce. To ship out with her I must step back a thousand years in history—maybe two thousand. She was bound on a classic voyage such as the Semitic seamen of the Persian Gulf and south Arabia had been making for centuries, to the emporia of the tropical Indian Ocean, buying and selling at wayside bazaars in scattered ports wherever the favoring monsoon blew. She would be gone six months at least—maybe longer. She had neither accommodation nor, indeed, shelter of any kind. Her cookhouse was a firebox on deck. A compass was her sole concession to modernity, and that was from the eighteenth century. She had two great sails set on lashed-up yards made from lithe Persian trees, and her masts were solid boles of Malabar teak—massive, enormous.

But she had the lines of a clipper and the grace of a sea bird; her skirted mariners handled her with competence and pride. The sheik who was her master was a prince among seamen in the trades he knew, and all around her dwelt an atmosphere of adventure, of far-off days and ancient voyaging. And, as far as I could find out, I was the first European to set out on such a voyage in so great a dhow since Marco Polo.

I looked forward immensely to the voyage. This was the way to learn. I had already been years in European ships both sail and steam, and I had sailed with the Polynesians among their islands, sailed my own ship around the world by Good Hope and the Horn, by way of the East Indies and the West, the South Seas and the South Atlantic.

When the Portuguese pioneers first burst into Indian Seas toward the end of the fifteenth century, they found a great

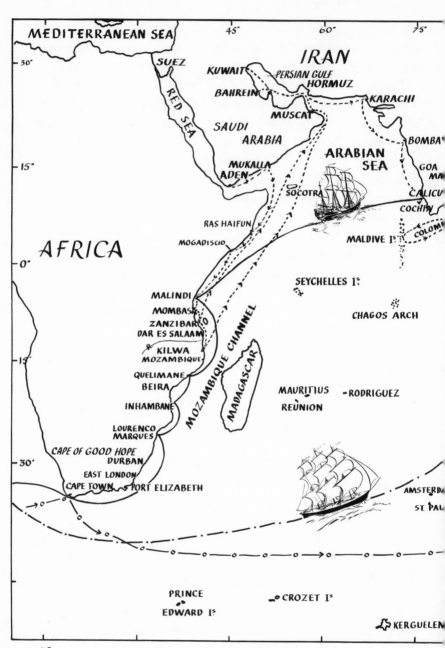

MEDITERRANEAN SEA

SUEZ

RED SEA

SAUDI ARABIA

AFRICA

IRAN

KUWAIT
PERSIAN GULF
HORMUZ
BAHREIN
MUSCAT
KARACHI

ADEN
MUKALLA

ARABIAN SEA

BOMBAY

GOA
MA

SOCOTRA

CALICUT
COCHIN
COLOM

RAS HAIFUN

MOGADISCIO

MALDIVE I.

SEYCHELLES I.

CHAGOS ARCH.

MALINDI
MOMBASA
ZANZIBAR
DAR ES SALAAM
KILWA
MOZAMBIQUE
QUELIMANE
BEIRA
INHAMBANE
LOURENCO MARQUES
CAPE OF GOOD HOPE
DURBAN
EAST LONDON
CAPE TOWN
PORT ELIZABETH

MOZAMBIQUE CHANNEL

MADAGASCAR

MAURITIUS
REUNION
RODRIGUEZ

AMSTERDA
ST. PAUL

PRINCE EDWARD I.

CROZET I.

KERGUELEN

ARAB DHOW VOYAGES -·>-·-,--·->--·-
VASCO DA GAMA ——————
EAST INDIAMEN ——·——·——
DUTCH INDIAMEN →—o—o—o

CALCUTTA

BAY
OF
BENGAL

RANGOON

ANDAMAN
I⁵

NICOBAR I⁵

SUMATRA

BORNEO

JAVA

PHILIPPINES

CELEBES

NEW
GUINEA

COCOS OR
KEELING I⁵

INDIAN

OCEAN

AUSTRALIA

N
W   E
S

TASMANIA

J. MITCHESON

29

Asian commerce long established. Arab, Persian, Indian deep-sea sailing ships, big dhows such as this I sailed in, carried on regular voyages between Arabia and the coasts of India, between India and east Africa down as far as Zanzibar and the coast of Mozambique, from Ceylon to the mouth of the Euphrates, from the Maldive Islands to the Gulf of Suez. Chinese junks—able, seaworthy, stoutly built ships—were known from their own ports to Mogadiscio, on the coast of East Africa, up the Gulf of Siam, and around the Malay Archipelago. Indian fleets had made great voyages to colonize Java, to trade wherever the favoring monsoon blew. Arab argosies had been carrying the spices of the East for transshipment to Europe down the ages.

All this commerce was old before a single small ship was evolved in Europe. A Greek merchant named Hippalus stumbled upon it centuries before Christ was born. Noticing, he thought, that the trade depended on two regular seasonal winds called monsoons, he claimed their "discovery."

The northern area of the Indian Ocean is peculiarly served by good sailing conditions and assured good weather during half the year. A northeast wind blows more or less steadily, never at storm strength, rarely dropping away to calm, never varying greatly in direction. That northeast wind blew sailing ships from the Persian Gulf to Ceylon, from the home town of the Queen of Sheba down to Zanzibar and the coasts of Tanganyika, from the incense coasts of South Arabia to the Comoro, Laccadive, and Maldive islands, from the merchants' seaport centers of the Persian Gulf to the great market ports of Calicut and Cochin.

When the northeast wind was not blowing it was replaced by a southwest almost as regular but not at all as tractable or steady, not a good sailing wind, for it could bring bad storms. But a well-kept ship could run homeward before it, wing back from Africa or India to Arabia in a matter of days.

An unknown Greek stumbling on all this in the first century of our era wrote a book about it which still survives. His name is lost but his book isn't. It is called the *Periplus of the Erythraean Sea* and it is a sort of directory of the monsoonal waters of the Indian Ocean. It names ports, lists trades, gives distances, courses, routes. In various translations, it is still in print. I had a copy when I joined the dhow. I showed it to our grand captain. He had a better, he said, diving into his huge sea chest and producing an elderly volume in handwritten Arabic. This, too, listed courses, distances, routes, provided hand-drawn sketches of the principal landmarks the whole way from the mouth of the Euphrates down to Dar-es-Salaam, all capes and headlands and turning points. Afterward examination by experts at the British Museum showed that it was on paper at least four centuries old.

Our captain still used it. With it alone he could find his way down Africa. But he did not refer to it a great deal. He knew the way, he said; and indeed he did, for he had been sailing there in the summers since he was eight, first with his father and other relatives, then as a sort of junior officer. He had never sailed as seaman. Always he had a piece of the officers' bench right aft, the abode of the privileged, the officer caste, to which no common seaman could aspire.

The voyage to the far-side market towns [the ports of east Africa] is made from Egypt about the month of July [wrote the author of the *Periplus*]. And ships are customarily fitted out from places across this sea [the Indian Ocean] bringing to these far-side market towns the products of their own places —wheat, rice, ghee, sesame oil, cotton cloths, girdles, and honey from the reed called sacchari. Some make the voyage specially to these market towns, and others exchange their cargoes while sailing along the coasts.

From Egypt ships would have to set out early to work their way down the Red Sea. Here the wind blows usually from the north at the Suez end and from the south at the other end; a sailing ship would have to tack into the wind or work her way slowly along inside the reefs with land and sea breezes to make the twelve hundred miles down to open sea.

No Egyptian ship does this now, nor has for some centuries. There is an account carved into an ancient Egyptian temple wall of a voyage ordered by a queen named Hatshepsut about fifteen hundred years before the birth of Christ to a mysterious land called Punt which scholars now cannot quite place. The queen sent a small fleet down the Red Sea, and they brought back cargo enough (according to the account) to fill a ten-thousand-ton cargo liner. Thirty-one myrrh trees complete with roots, tusks of ivory from huge African elephants, ebony, cassia, gold, cinnamon bark, animals enough to fill a zoo were all crowded aboard. Dogs, leopards, giraffes, baboons, cattle by the hundreds were marched up the gangplank to be stowed safely somehow in five small ships. How fresh water was carried for all these the temple pictures don't say. The animals are shown marching docilely aboard, and it is left at that. How all the oarsmen and crew found water enough is not indicated either. It seemed odd that such small ships could carry both large herds of animals and the men to tend them and fresh water sufficient for the lot.

For the solution of mysteries such as this I kept my eyes open aboard that big Kuwait dhow for many days, over many thousand miles. I sat on my piece of carpet on six feet of the officers' bench, right in the high end of the long poop and watched, listened, read, learned, month after month.

deck or in the stowed boats, ate dried shark and rice they ha
brought with them, yelled, quarreled, prayed, argued, slept
all day long. They paid, I learned, about two dollars for the
trip from Arabia to Africa, anywhere, but they brought their
own food, survived the best way they could, and got quickly
out of the way when the long-gowned mariners rushed about
the decks at the work of trimming sails.

The mariners always rushed. Day or night, they galloped
at the whispering of an order, leaping at a furious headlong
speed over and upon the passengers. The Lord help anyone
who might get in their way.

I had not bargained on these passengers. Leaving Aden we
had aboard only a few superior merchants, lean and bearded
gentlemen in long brown gowns, who had silvered daggers with
blood-thirsty curves buckled to stout belts around their slim
waists. One had a sword and shield. There were only four of
them. They seemed nice chaps, very quiet-spoken and man-
nerly. Some had chests of trade goods, silks and cotton stuffs
and the like, perhaps a little hashish, to sell in the bazaars of
Africa. One was tended by a wild little boy who had been en-
gaged on the beach at Ma'alla, aged about eight.

There were plenty of these wild boys, cheerful, bright little
chaps, homeless, living by their own efforts lawful or unlawful,
who fended for themselves and knew how to do it. They were
prepared to engage themselves with merchants going anywhere by dhow or camel caravan, for they had no homes, nothing to lose. I never knew whether they were orphans, runaways,
or just abandoned.

At Mukalla and a place called Shihr in south Arabia we
took aboard a Bedouin tribe, a host of Arab merchants of all
kinds, and another hundred or so migrants bound, they hoped,
for anywhere in east Africa. The belongings of the lot would
fit in one cabin trunk. The wiry Bedouin were dressed in black

It was fascinating. From there I had an uninte
of the whole of the ship. Neither deckhead nor
could obstruct my view, for there were none. All
the open, in full view of everyone, except when on
harem embarked for a week or two. The women an
locked up down below and never once emerged.

If I had really known just how tough that six-mo
voyage was going to be I might have thought tw
going. The Arab sailor is *tough* in a way modern con
have softened out of all of us. He had no clothes o
those he stood in and no bedding. He washed in the
under the stars, ate with the right hand and perform
tions with the left. The ship took her water whereve
nothing, usually from the wells of mosques where the
washed their feet. It was brought aboard in elderly skin
tied into wooden tanks which, I saw, soon became q
teresting aquariums. Food consisted mostly of rice, cur
fish from the sea, with a Somali sheep or African goa
monthly, slaughtered in the mornings and made into a r
stew by noon. Delicacies such as the eyes or a handful
from the tail (Somali sheep develop fat tails and are
prized for this reason) were tossed nonchalantly in my
tion. Ugh! I tried to pretend to like them but they came
making me sick.

We drank thimblefuls of very sweet tea in minute gla
pints of clove-flavored coffee in even smaller cups, and no w
at all—which was probably just as well. We shipped passeng
by the hundreds for whom there were no facilities and no
tention of providing any. They accepted the ship as St. Pa
and his fellow prisoners had had to do long years before, in t
Mediterranean. They slept where they could on a piece of th

"First-class" passengers take their ease on the big boom's poop, among the sea chests out of the crew's way. Turbaned figures are Omani merchants.

sarongs, daggers, and a kind of black dye which, their chief told me, kept off the heat by day and the cold by night. The sea stores for forty of them came aboard in a half of one old oil drum and did not fill that. They made their coffee flavored with cardamoms which kept down the gnawing stomach pains of hunger. They were quiet, orderly, well disciplined, and uncomplaining. It was the more affluent who did the shouting and fault-finding.

Not that that did them any good. Our captain ruled them all with a monarchical arrogance and a firm hand. He read the law and dispensed rough justice. He kept a tight grip on everything. After all, there were only thirty in the crew and there were some two hundred passengers. They could have rushed the quarter-deck and taken the ship. Some passengers were armed, but none of the crew were.

But they were a peaceful lot, except for occasional yelling. Life was reasonably quiet and there never were serious troubles. The voices of the locked-up harem were never heard.

All that bothered me was dysentery, for a while, and a bout
or two of fever caught up with me in the Red Sea. I was blind
for a week or two. I don't really know for how long. It was
painful and worrying. There was no medical man and there
were no medical stores. The princely master allocated me a
slave named Yusuf. Yusuf was a nice old man who, I discovered
later, spoke Persian, Hindustani, Swahili, Tamil, and his own
Arabic. But he knew no English. He made weird brews of the
Lord knows what and bathed my eyes.

I recovered. At first the burning sunlight shone red on my
closed eyes. Then, gradually, I could see again. It was a relief.

The Arabs were very casual about matters of health. To them
there were the fit and the dead. Since all illnesses and acci-
dents and everything else were by the direct will of God, there
was nothing to be done about them save accept, preferably
with grace and always with patience. They were extremely
casual, too, in matters of hygiene. When one developed bad
running eyes from an infection which spread, their treatment
was to pass a yellow handkerchief around with which all who
cared to rubbed their own eyes. It was the yellow color that
mattered, Yusuf told me.

If you step a thousand years back in history you must take
the consequences—all of them. While my blindness lasted I
had to accept it with patience and forbearance, as all the Arabs
accepted whatever Allah brought to them.

Chapter 4 • **TRADE, NOT DISCOVERY**

WE SAILED FIRST FROM ADEN EASTWARD ALONG THE COAST OF Arabia, for we had to make several hundred miles before we could swing around the turning point of Cape Guardafui on northeast Africa and run down the coast toward the south. The ship was deeply laden with bulk salt, hundreds of big packages of Iraqi dates from the Basra River, cooking stones, a little incense, a bundle of rich carpets, and odd trade goods.

The dates, I gathered, were so important that the Kuwait ships were measured by their capacities for loading them. My dhow had a capacity of thirty-five hundred packages. The largest could take perhaps five thousand. The voyage had begun at the Basra River with a full cargo of dates which the ship peddled around the coasts of Arabia wherever there was prospect of being paid for them (which was not at all ports, by any means). The last of them were disposed of at Aden after the bulk had gone off by camel caravan toward somewhere in Ethiopia, from a place called Berbera, in Somaliland. A close relative of the captain went with them, doubtless to collect payment.

The dhow carried cargoes which the captain (or some merchant or group of merchants back of him) owned, and bought and sold for cash as she went along. The few dates we had left were an odd lot, not from the current season. I found out later that their real purpose was to serve as food for a gang of African laborers who were going to cut mangrove poles in the delta

37

Captain and merchant

of the Rufiji River to provide our homeward cargo, after the outward cargo was all sold.

But the captain would have sold them to any buyer fool enough to take them at any wayside port and picked up something else to feed the Africans.

It took time to find things out—a great deal of time. Well, I had time—twenty-four hours a day, and nowhere else to go.

It took no time at all to notice that, contrary to the ideas I had gained from books beforehand, the wind was dead ahead. The dhow was obviously not sailing with a favoring wind, for the wind was right in our faces. It blew along the coast of Arabia from the precise direction in which we had to go.

So we beat, and she lay up to the wind's eye beautifully. That big oiled dhow sailed better than a yacht. She ghosted with the flap of her graceful sails. She slipped along to windward a mere 45 degrees from the wind's true direction. The wind was forcing her on the land, and we sailed very close to it. A backdraft of a bit of a land breeze helped in the evenings, but many times we had to tack, to spin the ship around and head for a while off the land.

This maneuver she did gracefully and with ease, though it necessitated the whole great mainsail to be shifted over on its cumbersome yard on each occasion. The skirted mariners, singing as they rushed, took the ends of gear—sheets and shrouds and tacks and all those ancient things—and ran furiously about the decks like a football scrimmage gone mad. Others swung the big yard, switched over shrouds. All knew precisely what they were at, and among them got the huge, awkward sail shifted to its new position before the dhow lost forward way—which was faster than we could tack most of the European square-riggers I had been in.

I noticed how perfectly the gear had been made for just those maneuvers which the ship had to do, how well she worked, what a fine team the swarthy, piratical mariners really were. Sometimes she'd spin around just off the beach, and I could see the pale green tint of shallow water where she would so easily have grounded, half a ship's length away. I'd have been nervous with a European ship there. None of the Arabs turned a hair.

But what was all this about Hippalus, and the dhows sailing one way with one favoring wind, back with another? I soon saw that this must be a landlubber's idea, a theory put forward just because the two winds do blow. Landlubbers find it easy to understand a sailing ship going before the wind. It was obvious that with her splendid weatherly qualities and her perfect capacity for eating into the wind (so long as the weather was good) this dhow did not need a favoring breeze at all.

We had, indeed, got around Cape Guardafui before the northeast monsoon blew from astern. By that time we had been in other ports, had the decks filled with passengers, and had added to our cargo by buying jars of Hadhramaut honey, thousands of small fans, and other ventures which the ship or members of her crew thought might bring a profit in east African waterfront bazaars. Each seaman was entitled to the space necessary to stow one sea chest, in which he could carry trade goods of his own. These chests were arranged on either side of the poop, in two ranks, where the captain (and everybody else) could always see them.

With the wind behind us that great dhow winged out her lateen sail, lifted her sharp cutwater, and sang along in a smiling sea with a wake like a knife's edge. Upright and graceful, she ran through the days, her glorious great sail perfect in these most marvellous conditions, swollen with the speed-giving wind, lifting and pulling while the graceful underwater cleft the sea with as little disturbance as the bosom of an albatross. After the midday meal, when the passengers slept and none kept a wakeful eye save the dark quartermaster puffing at his hookah cross-legged at the wheel, the only sounds were the soft sighing of the monsoon wind and the swish of the sea as the dhow passed gently, shadowing the rippling, deep-blue water as she ran. This was the stuff! Maybe Hippalus was right, after all.

Right or wrong, this was most glorious sailing. I was glad that my blindness had passed and I could see.

We ran down before the northeast monsoon, a most gracious and reliable wind (at least just then) with Africa on our right hand, the open Indian Ocean on our left. Other dhows tried to keep us company for there were many in that trade, but none could keep up with this queen of ships sailed by an Arab sheik. No measurement of speed was kept. No one even glanced at any chart. The coast of Africa was chart enough. It was never far away, and the landmarks were plain. The sheik-captain knew it better than he knew the features of his four young wives. He knew the way of the sea in those parts, he said, and had precise knowledge of all the sets and currents, even local movements, with that monsoon.

He knew, and he knew he knew—no false modesty for him. When he swung in toward the land off a distinctive headland named, he said, Ras Haifun, and sailed at first directly at the land as if to smash the ship, none turned a hair. Even I took only a mild interest, for by that time I was well aware that he knew what he was doing, whatever he did.

Sure enough, soon we came to a pleasant anchorage. Over went the longboat, on went the sheik's fine raiment, and, with precisely the same strict attention to stylish detail as at Aden, he was rowed ashore, though no one watched except myself and some six hundred passengers in a nearby Trucial Oman boom.*

Whatever our captain did, he did in style.

As for that Trucial Coast boom, she was crowded more than any other vessel I had ever seen, even a Chinese ferryboat or a pilgrim ship at Jidda in the height of the season. That little double-ender was so crowded that over a hundred of her passengers were seated along her rails for the very good reason that they could not fit inboard. We had passed a few bodies in the sea outside, brown-gowned old Omani, barefooted and barelegged, who must have come from her.

This was a place called Haifun, of which I had never heard for the good reason that Haifun was its Arab name. On our maps it was Dante, an Italian place at the time, a roadstead on the Indian Ocean offering a bit of a bazaar ashore, a large salt works, and little else. Since we were largely loaded with bulk salt I wondered what we were doing there; our captain apparently had his reasons.

European occupancy of any place in Africa, India, or Arabia meant nothing to him. He regarded it as recent, temporary,

* A *boom* is a double-ended Persian Gulf sailing vessel.

In the Indian Ocean, migrants crowd along the rails because there is no room for them inboard.

and of only passing importance. He carried on his own activities with his own people, regardless. Mysterious gowned and hooded figures came aboard and crouched around the officers' bench aft like the conspirators which they very probably were. We landed a few bags of rice, some tins of ghee (which I noted had come originally from Holland), a few cooking stones and fans, a little honey.

What else we might have done I do not know and knew better than to ask, but we were there a week. The sheik was a little downcast when we left and complained at length that the Italians ashore were making business difficult for their illustrious and more worthy predecessors, such as himself.

We romped along again outside under the same ideal conditions, this time as far as Mogadiscio or Mogadishu, then the capital of Italian Somaliland. Here astute port officials kept wary eyes on all Arabs and their dhows. They could land and sell anything they liked and cleared with Customs, of course: the trouble was in collecting for it in exportable currency, or in goods that could be sold elsewhere. The Italian lira was weak, its export prohibited. Some hundred of our passengers had imagined that they were bound for Mogadiscio, but the ruling was that only those who could prove previous residence could go ashore. All others must remain in the dhow at her anchorage.

The wandering Arab rarely can prove anything to European satisfaction, is not interested, takes other steps. Most of our hundred did. Because of that or possibly the general difficulties of old-fashioned trade, our captain declared that we would go into no more Italian ports that voyage. Nor did we. We sailed to the south in full view of them, but did not pause in our stride.

Next stop was Lamu, a place on the coast of Kenya, a romantic and attractive little port more Arab than Arabia. There was a huge old Portuguese fort from the days of Portugal's dominance and narrow stone-flagged streets where picturesque houses leaned toward each other across the narrow way, and neighbors knew more of what went on in opposite houses than in their own.

I liked Lamu. A fleet of swift lateen-rigged boats sailed out of there to Mombasa and Zanzibar. The Greek *Periplus* said they were sewn together, not fastened with bolts or nails. On the beach I saw several with sewn hulls. Lines of coarse stitching joined the planks. A couple of old graybeard shipwrights were taking the frames out of one and putting new frames in.

"Then we will add new planks," they told me. "But this time we will not sew them. It is easier to secure them with nails."

In that way they would have a new ship absolutely identical in form with the old. Indeed, she would have the old ship's name and be regarded as that vessel, not at all as her successor. This, apparently, saved some slight bother about remeasuring, taxing, dues, and the like.

We got rid of the few remaining passengers who had wished to land in Italian territory but had not already done so. We got rid of all sorts of things I had not known were aboard. We sold salt, a few packages of dates, a boat which the ship's carpenter had been building aboard ever since the dhow had left Kuwait. The boat was sold for a thousand east African shillings. It was a nice boat with graceful lines, and it sailed well. The Arab shipwrights seemed incapable of producing anything which did not have sweet lines.

The carpenter had few tools, no workshop, no vise. His big toes were his "vise" and he worked by eye. He had no plans. He was a nice young chap named Khaleel. He told me he wanted to become a master dhow-builder at Kuwait, as his forefathers had been. Kuwait, he said, built the best dhows in the world, and he had already served a seven-years' apprenticeship in the dhow yards there.

At Lamu and Mogadiscio, I noticed another reason why our wild boys were brought along. They helped their old Sindbad masters to carry haberdashery ashore—rich veils and sarongs and gorgeous materials—by the simple means of lashing the stuff around their slim bodies beneath their grubby gowns. They could carry a surprising amount of the gossamer materials like that, and there were no formalities. The old Sindbads loather formalities.

From Lamu we romped to Mombasa, one of the great emporia of that coast. The native harbor was well filled with Arab, Persian, Lamu, and Indian dhows. Many of the Arabs were astonishingly small. Any craft that could float, apparently, could fill itself with passengers and a bit of cargo and sail down before the northeast monsoon. Our captain said there were a thousand in the trade, and two thousand more around the coasts of Arabia not counting fishermen, water dhows, or pearlers.

Life among the dhow crews at Mombasa and at Zanzibar was straight out of Arabian Nights. Our dhow being à distinguished vessel, it carried a special musician, one of the seamen, named Ishmael, who strummed a guitar and sang. He could sing all night and if he ever got a tune out of that guitar, I never recognized it.

Our captain fancied himself as a dancer. There were weekly parties aboard by night. The ship was cleaned and rich Persian carpets were spread over the deck. Ishmael sang, the serang and his assistants banged on drums, our captain and his brother dhow masters shuffled about, cavorted, and leaped in time with the music and seemed to have great fun. Mysterious visitors came from the shore. Our bearded Suri passenger with the sword and shield, who had melted away at Haifun, turned up again, still with sword and shield. He danced, too.

All night these ribaldries went on. There were never any women and there was no alcohol. They drank coffee and tea, and puffed at hookahs. A few chewed a little ghat. All the mariners sat around, laughing and shouting choruses, roaring with delight at some quirk of the captain.

Next morning they would be as fresh as sea birds and slaving away to get the cargo out and landed in the longboat. They did all the work of the ship. They handled all the cargo both in and out. They manned the longboat to tow the ship if it were calm or she had to move from an awkward anchorage. When the anchor cables—medieval stuff of great size but no great strength, twisted (by the sailors) from coconut fiber—were heaved in, two or three always leaped over the side and cleaned away the mud from the cables with their hands. They were all great swimmers. So were the passengers.

As we approached the appointed anchorage in the section of the harbor designated by harassed port officers for Arab and Indian dhows, all the passengers who had no papers for that place (or any other) hung in the water on the offshore side. As we anchored they swam quietly among the other dhows which were already cleared. When officials came aboard, our numbers were correct and papers in order. No one batted an eyelid; the Arabs treated all this as a great game. As we would come barging under sail among the dhows at the crowded anchorage, of course many of our sailors would have to jump overboard to carry lines. Who could tell passengers from seamen? They were dressed the same.

Zanzibar, said the sailors, was a glorious place—Cairo, Paris, and Baghdad rolled into a riotous one. Nobody wanted to leave. The captain stayed on there when at last we wandered out to sea again with the mate in charge, to sail into the delta of the Rufiji River and load a cargo of mangrove poles for the return to Arabia. Their country was very short of wood of all kinds, Khaleel, the carpenter, told me. These mangrove poles were used in building and determined the size of most upstairs Arab rooms.

I learned more of how the sailors worked the ship on the way to the Rufiji. We stopped a while at an island called Kwale where they rigged down the mainmast, hauled the ship ashore at high tide, dried her out, propped her up, and "paid" the bottom with a mixture of heated camel fat and lime. They applied this with their hands, singing and chanting boisterously all the while. Then they hauled her off again as the tide returned, re-rigged the main, and off we sailed into the dark, gloomy arms of the dreadful African river.

This was a place which had somehow escaped my attention when learning what passed for geography at school; after a while, I was very sorry to be no longer ignorant. It must be the worst delta in the world. It rained and rained, and the mosquitoes bit like flying dingoes. There were millions of them in search of death, anxious just to get one bite of human blood first. To brush one's arm killed thousands. Their soft bodies rolled off in a mess of black and blood—my blood. If a thousand died, ten thousand returned. The lure of human blood was too much for them and they never gave up their quest for it.

The river water was three parts mud and the muddy, sodden banks were three parts water. Evil, submerged beasts like hippo and big crocodiles overturned canoes, drowned mangrove cutters. Monkeys leaped in the jungle and sometimes jumped aboard, to create chaos. We built a thatched house over the poop but the rain soaked through. The only achievement of this roof was to keep out such breaths of air that blew. No longer did Ishmael strum his guitar, for the strings had parted and the wood warped. No longer did anyone do anything save bring in boatload after boatload of mangrove poles to try to fill the ship as quickly as possible and be gone.

We were there six weeks.

It was an ancient trade, they told me. Semitic seamen once knew all east Africa and south and west Africa as well. They knew there was free sea off the southern end of Africa, and a route that way to the Atlantic. The Greek's *Periplus* says as much. Beyond Zanzibar, it records, "the unexplored ocean curves around toward the west . . . and mingles with the western sea."

A fleet sailed by predecessors of the Arabs called Phoenicians once had sailed around Good Hope, our captain told me. They had done this thousands of years ago, blazed the trail and then left it, for such voyages took too long and there was no trade. Such a voyage would take years and be very difficult. The ships would have to be hauled ashore in suitable places like Kwale when caught in the strong-winds season, and the sailors would have to turn farmers for a while to grow a crop for food.

Well, they could do that—but not without hope of substantial profit. What sense was sailing for sailing's sake? Sailors were poor men, forced to go to sea for a living. Captains sailed ships for merchants' profit and their own. No profits, no sailing. They could not make profits by themselves, except with such stuff as timber. Timber had to be cut, seasoned, dragged to a beach, loaded. It paid little return on a really long voyage. Eastern sea trade relied upon established markets with stable government, where goods of value could be exchanged and debts lawfully enforced.

This Phoenician voyage is documented by the historian Herodotus, who seems not to have believed in it himself. Herodotus was a landsman. Phoenician seamen were great wanderers and traders. They could have made such a voyage well enough. So could Arabs. But, as our captain said, it made

Homeward bound from Rufiji, laden with mangrove poles

Alan Villiers

no sense. He sailed only on established routes for trade, not discovery. The Arabs always had done that—no more.

I could see his point.

From the Rufiji we staggered back deeply laden for Zanzibar. The captain was at length induced to part with the delights of the island. With song and dance after a wild night party of carpet-shuffling, our sturdy mariners got the huge yard hoisted, broke out the anchor, set the sail, and we were off. When those Kuwait seamen danced, beating their hard bare feet on the ship's teak deck, the whole dhow shook and trembled. They clapped their hands with a noise like thunder and seemed to draw stimulus and refreshment from the strenuous exercise like a form of Yogi. They danced as they worked, like demons.

But it was not yet the time of the southwest monsoon. What was all this about sailing down with the one, back with the other monsoon? How now, Hippalus? For we did nothing of the kind. We sailed down with the northeast and back with it, too, for the dhow could make the course both ways with that wind.

He wouldn't dream of waiting for the southwest monsoon, our captain said. Any fool knew that. The southwest brought bad weather, storms, poor visibility. It was no time for dhows to wander the open sea. They ran for the Persian Gulf or home ports in south Arabia before it broke.

We had sailed down always in sight of land—Africa on the right-hand side with its landmarks like signposts. Now we reversed the process and kept Africa on the left, slightly farther off but not much, for we did not intend to touch anywhere before reaching Muscat in the Persian Gulf, two and a half thousand miles away.

Chapter 5 • WITH THE PEARLERS

WE SAILED FROM ZANZIBAR TO MUSCAT, A PICTURESQUE, mountainous place with some large Portuguese forts, in three and a half weeks. The weather was good, the sailing simple. We were out of sight of land on only one day. This was the day we crossed from Cape Guardafui to the coast of south Arabia. This once sighted, we coasted along again, our captain ticking off the landmarks as we advanced. Some he gave a good berth—there were pirates there, he said, Bedouin wreckers who would cut the ship out if they could, for they were lawless and poor, and no strong sheik ruled over them—and others we passed close by.

So we came in due course to the turning point into the Gulf of Oman, and soon, sailing past the wicked port of Sur well out at sea (it was the worst place of the lot for pirates, the Kuwait Arabs said), we came to Muscat.

It was obvious that these Arab voyages were all coasting. The captain told me that he made voyages from the mouth of the Basra River to Karachi, Bombay, and Cochin and back again in the same way. He knew the landmarks; he had, he declared, sufficient local knowledge of such things as sets and odd quirks of currents, and indrafts into bays. I don't doubt he had. But what about fixing his ship's position sometimes? There was no need, he said; he knew where his ship was. And why did he carry no lights, as European vessels did? I was aware that he knew the international sea rules of the road, for the sultan

50

Alan Villiers

Working aloft the Kuwait boom. These Arabs need no footropes.

of Zanzibar's officers had examined him in that matter, and he had passed. (I sat for the examination at Zanzibar myself; it was not very difficult. The sultan's officers took the obvious view that any seaman who brought in a big dhow from Arabia or from India probably knew what he was at.)

As European vessels carried lights, said our captain, he need not, for he could see them and keep out of their way. That was his rule of the road. As for other dhows, sea-going Arab, Persian, and Indian ships all sailed the same way at the same time of the year. They knew where they were going, who else was around, and in the same winds they made the same speed. There was therefore little risk of collision. Besides, they had good eyes, and Allah was merciful. And lights were a fire risk anyway.

So we sailed on through the starry nights, dark or moonlit, with only the feeble glow of a binnacle lamp to light the compass card, and at rare intervals a very old lantern swung by Jassim, the cook, when he brought the night's clove-flavored coffee to the bench around the wheel.

Allah was merciful. This was in the last resort the answer to everything as we sat on our haunches and talked and argued around the officers' bench in the first night watch, while the great shape of the wind-filled sail quietly swept the dhow along beneath the stars. The captain, his brother the second mate, a hawk-nosed Kuwaiti who was a sort of minor second captain and chief mate, and the senior Sindbads among the merchants formed a discussion group which met nightly and talked together of philosophy, the message of their religion Islam, the curious ways of the white man and his temporary superiority which they were certain would soon be ended, at least in Asia.

The year was 1939. It was all most interesting.

I tried to think back through the two or three thousand years or more that similar sailing ships had been using this great highway of the Indian Ocean. In my mind's eye I could see the fleet of the Admiral Nearchus, moving the conquering Alexander's armies through the Persian Gulf in the year 326 B.C., slipping gracefully through the deep waters with that same monsoon that blew us.

In the mornings, sometimes, we were among a fleet of twenty or more big dhows, coming back from Africa and from India. They were a brave sight, and stirring. How marvelous must the sea have looked bearing Nearchus' fleet of thousands! Martial banners streaming multicolored in the sun, military trumpets blaring, the glint of the sun on spear points and shields, the indigo-blue sea creaming softly before their swift bows, combined to make a grand sight.

Alexander had sought to conquer all Arabia, sailing from his city-base of Babylon with an enormous fleet. Away back in those far-off days, the wealth of the Arab sailing trade was enormous.

The Sabaeans of South Araby—Araby the Blest—had "doors, walls, and roofs variegated with inlaid ivory, gold, silver, and precious stones," and basins and drinking vessels of solid silver and gold.

But Alexander died; his fleet sailed no more.

Instead of conquerors, now there were only traders.

We sailed in due course into Bahrein and sold the mangrove poles there to the agents of the King of Arabia, who was building a new palace at Ryadh. The cargo out and paid for, the dhow romped home through the well-known waters to Kuwait, her voyage done. Here she was rigged down and floated on a high tide behind a breakwater of coral by the picturesque waterfront. Mats were hung all around her sleek oiled hull to protect the teak from the hot summer sun, and the mariners having stayed to do all this, collected their few rupees and then went off to the pearling. The southwest monsoon blew in the Indian Ocean far outside, and Kuwait ashore was like a

With the pearling fleet in the Persian Gulf

Alan Villiers

furnace. No long-voyage dhow went to sea at that season.
Official figures showed 108 registered at the port.

I sailed a while with the pearlers, too, out to the banks off
Kuwait, then one of the largest sources of natural pearls in
the world. The pearling fleet was as interesting in its own way
as the deep-sea dhows. Pearling was carried on then by a fleet
of several hundred vessels, some small, some up to sixty or
seventy feet long, all crowded with men many of whom were
also deep-sea seamen. They sailed with the dhows in the sailing season and became pearlers at Kuwait.

Between the two they scraped a hard living, saw little of
their homes. They pearled only when the northern gulf waters
were at their warmest. The fleet moved out, under an emir of
the sea, an admiral who was a cousin of the ruling sheik; they
anchored on banks known for rich oysters, and the men went
down into the sea without diving gear or safety device of any
kind.

Hour after hour, day after day, week after week the same
men dived, working in two sections. One section made ten
dives while the other rested; the same tenders looked after
both, and the lines were kept clear on the big sweeps by which
the pearling vessels were usually propelled—one sweep for each
diver.

The diver had a nose-clip of sheep's horn which he secured
over his thin nostrils as he went down. That and a rough
basket for the oysters were all he had. He groped on the sea
bed, eyes open, lungs near bursting, grabbing up oysters by
hand. He went down on a stone to get down quickly. The
tender hauled up this stone again immediately he felt it ground-
ing: the diver clung onto his oyster basket, gave this a tug
when he could stand no more, and was hauled then swiftly to
the surface.

Here the poor man rested, panting, by the side of the dhow

Alan Villiers

Pearl divers at rest

and, at a signal and with the appropriate shout to Allah, the divers all flung their oyster baskets together on board with a sort of ritual. No oyster was opened then. The day's take accumulated to let the oysters die, they said; dawn next morning was the proper time for examining them. All hands, divers and tenders alike, were paid on shares. No diver had more than another, though all had more than the tenders. No man could claim any special pearl no matter how valuable, for none knew from whose basket it had come.

It was a hard life. The unfortunate divers, since they dived in their skins and stayed down more than a minute each time—I timed them—dared not eat a good meal even if one were available. (The tenders looked very well.) They kept going on drugged coffee and a little rice and fish, taken in the evenings when the day's work was done. Some got the "bends" and died. Others just died. They were buried on the beaches and their debts—they were always in debt by the system in use—passed to relatives.

I went down once. It was my first essay on the bottom of the sea. I hated it. It was frightening, awful. I could think of nothing good in the whole industry. My lungs felt like bursting. My nose bled when I came up (which was with the utmost speed), and my ears rang for days. I got two oysters and there was not even a seed pearl in either of them. I looked.

When the day's work was done, all the pearling craft made in to the nearest beach, for they were never far at sea. They anchored close in, and the greater part of the crews landed. The pearling ships were so crowded with men that all could not sleep aboard, and pearl-diving was a very wet business. So they had their evening meal ashore, then stretched out on the sand and slept.

I wondered whether this may have thrown light on that voyage of Queen Hatshepsut's of Egypt, to the Land of Punt. Her ships could have anchored off a beach one evening and the crews landed—even some of the animals. In this way they might carry water enough, for they would know where to find more. Fresh water turns up in odd places to those with the skill to find it and a desert background of want, like Arab seamen and Australian aborigines.

I had sailed a voyage with a small Red Sea dhow before shipping in the African trader. We went from Aden to a place called Gizan in the Red Sea, just across the Yemen border. We anchored every night, too, and moved ashore for brushwood for the evening fire, and sometimes to sleep. The sailors knew where to find a little water.

There was a place off one of the beaches not far from Kuwait where fresh water springs bubbled up in the salt sea. Divers went down to these springs with goatskins and filled them with sweet water. The supply seemed to be unlimited.

As I sat in the dawns watching the silent divers opening

their piles of smelly oysters, I reflected on what I had learned. Semitic seamen had sailed the monsoonal waters of the Indian Ocean for thousands of years. They had gone as far as Malaya and China, too, for these voyages could be made by coasting with favoring winds at the proper season. It was not difficult to learn these seasons. They were regular, and the sea winds blew home to the land. Chinese junks, able and seaworthy vessels which were stronger and larger than the Arabs', Indians', and Persians' dhows, made long voyages in the same way when political conditions ashore permitted. Marco Polo speaks of one junk in which he traveled with six hundred other passengers. Such Eastern voyages are well documented. There is no doubt of them.

But, on reflection, it seemed to me that the whole lot were more or less glorified coasting with a few short sea-hops. Except for the Indians who crossed the open sea from the Malabar coast to East Africa and the odd Arab who might have done likewise, and the open-sea run across the Bay of Bengal, the

Open-decked, low-waisted small dhow sailing out of Aden

Alan Villiers

whole of those voyages could be made in sight of land, as ours was in that modern Kuwait dhow. Her captain could not navigate at all, in the sense of finding his way over the open sea. He made no use of astronomical navigation, though his predecessors had done so. He had forgotten how. He never once as much as tried to find his compass error. To him the compass needle was always true. Though a good seaman he had his limitations, and they were severe. The Chinese and the Indians, the Malays and Indonesians sailed also with the seasonal winds they knew and understood. There was a tradition of one Chinese who was, allegedly, driven in a storm across the Pacific to a harbor which may have been San Francisco. Such a voyage if made led to nothing. It was accidental, a blowaway, a non-repeatable miracle.

The Asiatics, have no doubt, had early made a great step forward in man's use of the sea and the development of ships. All this great sailing commerce of theirs was flourishing while Europe slept; but it was in essence a sort of fringe sailing under God-sent good conditions. Allah was merciful, indeed. Though the zone of the steady southeast trade winds bordered the well-sailed monsoon seas, no Arab, Persian, Babylonian, Chaldean, Sumerian, or Indian ventured there. The whole north Pacific offered circulatory sailing—eastward with the west-wind zone north of the trades, back again to the west with the favoring trades which blow there from the northeast—which could have been the basis of ocean voyages. There were ancient civilizations in Mexico, Central America, and Peru with which useful contact could be made.

No such voyages, as far as we know, were ever made. The Asiatics, being sensible seamen who had to earn a living, sailed to the markets they knew. They sailed and traded for the riches of the East, which were great and inexhaustible. In the world they knew, what else was there? Where else to go?

Old print of the *Keying*—a junk that sailed around the Cape of Good Hope

The trades they profited by they had themselves established, and their ships were quite suitable for their continued exploitation. For really long voyages beyond that zone they were not suitable at all.

As for the long voyages of the peoples we now know as Polynesians, these were in quite a different category. They probably began by enforced migrations, accidental blowaways of a primitive, happy people, who sought first only some land to live upon. If it had water, fish, coconuts, it sufficed for them. In time, they made voyages among their own island groups with which much of the tropical South Pacific is almost littered. They reached New Zealand. They sailed somehow to Hawaii— a far cry from anywhere in Asia; a long way, indeed, from anywhere. But there is no evidence that they ever made really long voyages deliberately at all, to anywhere. It was canoe-borne castaways who drove to New Zealand—brave and able seamen and good colonizers, certainly. It was canoe-borne castaways who spread among the islands, skimming across the sea in their big canoes.

Many of the islands are high. In clear weather they can be seen for the best part of a hundred miles. (I have seen Tahiti at this distance from the deck of a sailing ship.) Many of the Society Islands, Samoa, the New Hebrides, Solomons, Fijis, Rarotonga, the Marquesas, the Australs, Rapa, and the islands off New Guinea's eastern end are high and mountainous, good landfalls from the surrounding islands of the same group or for castaways from atolls in their latitudes. Atolls, on the other hand, are low, easily lost to view when islanders are blown off in a storm. There are always more atolls for castaways to find. By no means were all inhabited when the Europeans first came to the South Seas.

The way of life of the Pacific islanders populated their islands, not their habits of trade or the excellence of their ships for ocean voyaging, for they had neither real trade nor real ships. A canoe is not a ship no matter how large, nor how many warriors might be packed aboard for a warlike excursion.

As for the theory put forward by some raft-builders from Norway in recent years that—as they themselves managed once to do—the Polynesians came from Peru with the favoring winds and currents that blow and drift from that direction, seamen think this most unlikely. South America is a continent; why sail off from there thousands of miles into the blue? Why should anyone want to do that, *dare* to do it or, trying in primitive craft so hazardous a passage, bring it safely off? From a continent to islands? For this is difficult navigation, indeed.

From the westward, from Asian waters, the islands and the island groups stretch in useful and complementary line. If you missed one you would find the next, or the next. But from the coast of Peru to the high land of Tahiti is over forty-two hundred miles and the atolls of the Tuamotu, assuming them to be found, are little nearer.

What sailing raft not provisioned by the United States Navy and equipped with all its needs could survive that far? Or what canoe not similarly fortunate? The intervening seas offer nothing but fish and sea birds. To try such a voyage over so great a distance implies prior knowledge of some place to go, somewhere to make for which can be found. What evidence is there that any seafaring race capable of such voyaging (or any deep-sea voyaging at all) ever lived on the west coast of South America? People with a continent to exploit move about in it, find somewhere to live in it, need not rush away by sea. A voyage from the west coast of South America to the Polynesian islands of the South Seas would have been a greater, nobler effort than the epoch run of Christopher Columbus in 1492—a thousand miles farther, a miracle of navigation. In a raft? I don't believe it.

Look at the seas on the other side of South America, the South Atlantic, with its high islands of Trinidad, St. Helena, Ascension, South Georgia, the Falklands, Tristan da Cunha. Not one of these was inhabited when European seamen first came upon them.

It would be a fool indeed who, unless forced, changed a mainland for any of these. It would, I think, be just as foolish to sail westward with the southeast trade winds from Chile or Peru—foolish and fatal.

The trading voyages around their own islands or atoll groups were remarkable achievements and require no later embellishment. The Europeans who first visited their islands were amazed at Polynesian canoe voyages and the knowledge of chiefs about the Pacific in their own immediate area. The great English discoverer James Cook once found Tahitians on an island called Atiu, six hundred miles from Tahiti. But they were survivors from a canoe blown off course in a tropic storm while voyaging locally among their own islands; once having made Atiu, quite accidentally, they could not sail back again. Cook and others found Polynesians who could name, and place, upward of a hundred other islands, but always within an area of a few hundred miles.

If the Polynesians were really the skillful navigators some theorists have suggested, and the Maoris of New Zealand maintained a sailing link with the Society Islands from whence they are supposed to have come, it is odd that some of them, at least, did not carry on to the rich coast of tropical Australia. Here a continent awaited their exploitation. In New Zealand's north island they were well placed to make such a voyage, if their canoes could survive it. It lay to leeward in the Coral Sea trade winds.

There is no evidence that any ever did.

The largest South Seas canoe was essentially unseaworthy, like all canoes—all right in quiet seas and good weather but dangerous and hopeless in rough seas. I have sailed in several, both in the South and North Pacific. In bad weather they swamp; the lashings of outriggers and twin hulls, platforms and masts work adrift; and the canoes can easily overturn.

We have taken a firsthand look at Asian and some Pacific waters, have seen some remarkable mariners and interesting vessels.

But we must look elsewhere to continue the story of man's conquest of the sea.

Chapter 6 • **THE ANCIENT MEDITERRANEAN**

THE MEDITERRANEAN WAS THE CENTER OF EUROPEAN CIVILI-
zation. Surrounded by habitable and mostly fertile lands with
long coastlines well provided with ports, blessed with a pleasant
summer sailing season, its blue and frequently placid surface
is sprinkled with useful high islands like Crete, Cyprus, Malta,
Sicily, Corsica, Sardinia, the Balearics and Dodecanese. Several of the islands are very large. The Mediterranean was a
good sea road for early sailing commerce. There are many bib-
lical references to its great ports and sea commerce, and there are
further references, which have come down to us in the works
of several of the old historians.

The Phoenicians, a daring and competent race of seafaring
masters and merchants from the eastern Mediterranean, were
probably the first ocean voyagers. There is the story in Herodotus of their voyage around Africa from east to west, from the
northern end of the Red Sea back to the "Pillars of Hercules"
at the western entrance to the Mediterranean. There is an account of an Egyptian king called Snefru sending a fleet of
forty Phoenician ships to bring back logs cut in the forests of
the Lebanon. And there was Hanno the Carthaginian—
Carthage was founded by the Phoenicians—who sent off a
squadron of Phoenician ships to make a voyage around Africa
from the west, as the Pharaoh Neccho had commissioned his
countrymen to do likewise the other way around.

Hanno's fleet sailed out past Gibraltar to oblivion: we know no more about it. Carthaginian coins have been found on an island in the Azores, well out in the Atlantic. These probably dropped from the rotted sea chests of some drowned Phoenicians whose driven-off ship had somehow fetched up there, with the winds and the currents. Living Phoenicians dropped no coins. They were smart, able businessmen, good at driving bargains and most zealous in guarding the secrets of their hard-won trades—so much so that in the end they were too successful, for no real record of them has yet been found. Not as much as the log of a single ship nor a good representation of one, not a chiseled tablet that could be a manifest, or a letter home has been discovered.

One may imagine them with their graceful long ships driving in with the Atlantic swell through the Strait of Gibraltar, purple sails swelling triumphant in the westerly breeze and great, raised prows—always surmounted with the carved and fearsome figure of a horse's head—high above the foaming waves at their bows. The merchants aft on the raised poop counted their gold and reckoned their profits, much like the old Sindbads of my Arab dhow, and the seamen looked forward to the pleasures of Carthage, of Tyre or Sidon. One may catch a brief, hazy picture of these remarkable ships and seamen, but that is all. It is recorded that they did much sailing for the Egyptians, who seem not to have cared for active seafaring themselves. The priests, says Plutarch, gave their opinion that "to sail from Egypt was one of the most unholy of things." They must have been landlubbers. One of the fates they feared was not to be buried properly.

The Phoenicians first came to prominence, apparently, because they had control of the trade in purple dyes, which were made from a shellfish found on their coasts. Purple then was a rare color, greatly admired and much prized. Purple robes brought big prices, and marked the highest ranks. Only Phoe-

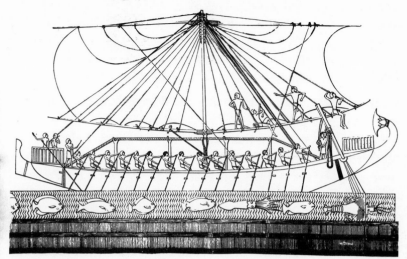

Egyptian ship, about 1600 B.C.

nicians could afford to use purple dyes in such mundane things as sails and then only on very special ships—perhaps to impress those sea-critical priests. The shrewd Phoenicians, too, as the landlubber Egyptians waxed richer and richer, produced a dye of a beautiful lapis-lazuli blue. From this they made cosmetics for rich Egyptian women, who dyed their eyelids with the thrilling blue and brushed their eyelashes with another Phoenician cosmetic known, apparently, as *stibium.*

Gold and silver; cedarwood for making stout doorways, furniture, and ships; ivory and linens and other rich raiment; vases from Crete; spices from the Far East to enrich Egyptian meats; turquoise and copper from the mines of Sinai; tin to make bronze from far-off Britain—in all these things the Phoenicians traded, cornering the market if they could, making tremendous profits. They provided fighting galleys for the conquering Persian king Xerxes, supplying half the fleet which was rousingly defeated by the Greeks at Salamis near Athens in the year 480 B.C. This Salamis affair was one of the decisive battles in the story of the world. Had the Persians won, the glories of ancient Greece would never have been allowed to flower.

An ancient Suez canal aided the Phoenicians in their eastern trade. As early as 1400 B.C. there is a record of a ditch being dug to connect the Nile with the Bitter Lakes, along which ships of the day could be dragged when the Nile waters were high. Over a thousand years later, in 285 B.C., Ptolemy Philadelphus cut a canal which ran from the Mediterranean to the Red Sea by way of a bend of the Nile. Herodotus tells of 120,000 forced laborers losing their lives to excavate yet another version of an early canal across the isthmus dividing Egypt from Canaan.

But the Phoenicians—like others before and after them—grew too prosperous, became fat, were overthrown; their sailing secrets died with them. Greek merchantmen and Romans succeeded them. These kept to the Mediterranean. The Greeks appear to have specialized in galleys and developed them to a high pitch with many rows of sweating oarsmen—up to five and more, say the records. Antiquarians and nautical archaeologists still puzzle over the manner in which these galleys could possibly have been rowed. How were so many men in so many banks arranged so that all worked efficiently with manageable oars?

There are plenty of pictures on ancient Greek vases of craft called biremes, snout-headed galleys with two banks of oarsmen and a platform built above them where landsmen fought. There were other fighting galleys known as quinqueremes, apparently with five banks of oars and the same platform. Oarsmen could move a smooth, clean galley through quiet water at a good rate, but only for the briefest of periods. It was heavy work, and back-breaking. Greek galley hands were free men, not driven by sadists with lashing whips.

Their ships also had a mast and a big square sail, as the Vikings had. They lowered masts and sails when going into battle, and they pulled the galleys up on a friendly beach by night for so great a horde of men could not live or cook their meals aboard.

Galleys were for good weather, smooth seas, short passages. In war they were fought at sea like cavalry ashore, and their fighters and commanders were military men who fired arrows, hurled javelins, rocks, or wads of flaming fire. Often galleys had ram-bows that were especially strengthened and carved in the forms of wild beasts. They would rush at each other, oars flashing with rhythmic perfection, trumpets blaring, soldiers tensed. The galley master tried to cut into the other's hulls amidships to let the sea flood them or, failing that, to knock away the banks of oars down one side and then dash in again swiftly to the knockout blow while the opponent spun unmanageable in temporary but fatal impotence. Fleets of them formed defensive circles, all their ram-heads facing outward, all their soldiers ready with stuff called Greek fire—a flaming naphtha mixture easy to ignite and very hard to extinguish. Or, at times, they rigged up machines aboard like wooden towers which could hurl big rocks, to crash through the opposing oarsmen and their thwarts and pierce the bottom planking.

Galley battles were swift and furious affrays. The army men liked them, for they did not feel "at sea." This was the land warfare they well understood, carried to the sea—a fight between big sea beasts driven by oars but in fact existing only to carry opposing soldiers into positions favorable for destroying their enemies by well-established means. There were well-known drills and formations. One side did this and the other that.

At Salamis, the Greek leader Themistocles threw the great

fleets of King Xerxes into fatal confusion when, in local waters he well knew, he did not fight his galleys according to the established rules. He enticed the enemy into narrow waters, let the sea breeze get up and toss them about, robbing the soldiers of their footholds and their balance. Then he fell on them with his own ordered lines of galleys which were able to operate in quiet waters, and decimated them a few at a time. Soon the sea was littered with overturned and smashed-up Phoenician galleys and their oars, and the bodies of oarsmen. The soldiers sank at once, borne down by their heavy armor.

Pressing in around a headland from sea came more and more of the Xerxian aggressors, for their morale was high. They rowed in, sure of victory, and they were unable to see what had happened to the others until it was too late. King Xerxes himself had his golden throne mounted on a hill from which he planned to watch every detail of his glorious victory; there he sat, together with scribes with stone tablets to write down his remarks and record the names of captains who distinguished themselves. Two captains, washed ashore from their destroyed galleys, climbed the hill to apologize and "explain" to Xerxes how they had been taken in.

"Off with their heads!" snapped the king.

He could see for himself.

After that, his fleet decimated and the Greek fleet still intact, he had to withdraw his armies and get out of the Mediterranean. The battle of Salamis was an early example of the importance of sea power. The mightiest army in the world, once committed to action beyond the sea, was useless if it did not maintain also a victorious fleet to assure command of the sea.

Galleys were popular in the Mediterranean for the following two thousand years. They were popular with land-based gen-

Vase painting of a Greek ship from the sixth century B.C.

erals turned into temporary admirals. (The word *admiral* comes from the Arabic *emir-al-bahr*, ruler of the sea. *Emir-al* became *admiral*—emir of nothing. Some landlubber left out the sea, perhaps deliberately in those early days, for admirals and generals were for centuries considered interchangeable.)

The French navy was still using galleys in the Mediterranean in the early nineteenth century. So were Sweden and Russia in the Baltic. Galleys had the obvious advantage in the days of the sailing ship of being fully maneuverable in calms. They could avoid rocks and shoals. In action, they could sneak up on becalmed or slowly moving ships, hit them with heavy rams, close in and pour a small army aboard. For short hauls, their commodious decks could carry large numbers of military; slaves could row them. As the years passed they were usually armed with heavy cannon placed well forward where they could send a murderous short-range fire unobstructed by the ship's own hull or her rigging. The guns—generally, at least one was of enormous caliber—were aimed by aiming the galley herself, swinging her about with the great sweeps that propelled her.

Sailing ships had guns, too, of course, but these stuck through their sides behind lidded sections of the hull called gunports. They could fire only outward, each battery on its own side. If the ship was becalmed the guns could not be aimed at all. They had to be fired directly abeam, at 90 degrees or so from whichever way the ship pointed. For centuries ships' guns were cumbersome, chancy things. Galleys had a great advantage, for they could row in from ahead or astern, rake the sailing ship with heavy fire, and then pour their soldiers aboard.

As the centuries passed big galleys sprouted masts and sails, too—the heavy mast and lateen rig of the Moslem Arabs who overran the Mediterranean. Most galleys were for war or piracy, or both, but the city ports of medieval Italy also developed a larger type for commerce. Florentine galleys made annual trading voyages between Florence and Flanders, via Spain, Portugal, France, and England, bringing spices and the riches of the East, taking back wool and woolen cloth. These big trading galleys relied mainly on sails. The oars were auxiliary. Their English port was Southampton.

There were by no means only galleys in Mediterranean waters. In the great days of Rome—though the Romans themselves were never seamen—there were two kinds of ships, the fighting, short-range galley and the round-bellied, long-range sailing merchantman. The round ships used to sail to Alexandria for Egyptian corn, and between the eastern and central Mediterranean, generally. There are many sculptured representations of them: we can see quite well what they looked like—distinctive, well-built, solid vessels often a hundred feet long, with spacious saloons on the deck to accommodate rich passengers, capacious holds to carry large cargoes, a simple rig of one large sail on a squat mainmast and a smaller, balancing sail on a leaning mast forward called the *artemon*.

As Rome prospered and its leading citizens were able to lead more and more luxurious lives, some of these potbellied little cargo-liners were fitted with extraordinary lavishness. Consuls and important merchants traveled by them, for the galley of those days was of too restricted a range. One reads of Roman roundships with luxurious, tiled bathrooms, outside terraces around the rich, beautifully fitted cabins where vines grew; and early "air conditioning" was provided by slaves who swung large fans. Life in such a vessel, sailing the summer seas while a dominant Rome kept peace, must have been good.

St. Paul was wrecked out of one of these ships, but not a luxury liner. His ship was wrecked because she was trying to bring him for trial in Rome too late in the sailing season. In a storm, the master ran her ashore under her *artemon*, with a primitive anchor dragging aft to keep her straight. It was good seamanship, the only thing he could really do when his awkward vessel with its important passenger got hopelessly on a lee shore.

What a great trade there was in those far-off days!

"Gold and silver and precious stones, and pearls and fine linen, and purple and silk and scarlet, and all sweet wood and all manner vessels of ivory . . . and cinnamon, and odors and ointments of frankincense, and wine and oil and fine flour, and wheat and beasts and sheep and horses, and chariots and slaves," as the chronicler in Revelation lists the trade of Rome, "wherein were made rich all that had ships in the sea."

But Rome burned. Its empire passed away. Its fleets of roundships became in time the potbellied merchantmen of the Middle Ages, carrying humdrum merchandise for the most part, though, until the end of the fifteenth century, Venetian vessels made their merchants rich by monopolistic carriage of the spices of the East.

In recent years, wrecks of a number of ancient ships have been discovered by skin divers and by other modern diving methods in Mediterranean waters. Though the centuries of immersion have rotted their timbers and the sea growth has overwhelmed them, here and there the original hull form can be made out. From more than one her spilled cargo has poured out through rock-torn holes in the hull and lies there on the sea floor—big jars called *amphorae* which once were filled with wine or olive oil. There must have been an immense trade in these standardized jars of valued liquids. The best way of moving them in bulk was by sea.

Later—much later—came the fleets of the Saracens, Moslems inspired by the prophet Mohammed, sweeping the peace-loving and the established before them as they overran the Mediterranean. To attack them, in due course, came the fleets of the Crusaders into that history-rich sea. Many of these coasted down from the English Channel, sailing in the summers, with all the pageantry of knighthood, sometimes under royal admirals. It was not until the amazing Battle of Lepanto, seventeen years before the Spanish armada sailed for England, that the Saracen fleets were at last decisively defeated—twelve hundred years and more since the last Roman ship had disappeared beneath the seas or collapsed, a wornout, rotted hulk, in the Tiber mouth by Ostia, the port of ancient Rome.

Long, long before Lepanto another sailing people had broken into the Mediterranean—wild, fierce men with swift and fearsome long-ships and bloody ferocity in battle unequaled even by the Saracens. These were the notorious Scandinavians called Vikings, a lean and virile race of sea rovers who really could handle ships, and did.

Until they appeared on the scene, the Mediterranean sea story was much as that of the Asian waters, of seasonal voyaging in established trades in a confined sea. Knowledge had leaped ahead. The compass-needle had come from China. The Greek philosophers and geographers had reasoned that the world was a sphere, that it could be sailed around, that too far east was west.

But no one sailed very far, either way.

After those secretive monopoly-seekers, the Phoenicians had found no useful trade routes around the south of Africa, no other voyagers went that way or, as far as we know, on any real ocean voyages. There is neither evidence nor any strong tradition of such things among the Mediterranean peoples. Their ships carried on what was really a limited trade, a glorified coasting with short sea-hops from one long coastline toward another whose landmarks were even better defined than those of the monsoon seas of the Indian Ocean and the signposts of the sea route to China. An early lighthouse or two were added for good measure. The pharos at Alexandria was one of the wonders of the ancient world. All it was, indeed, was a convenient structure 312 feet high with a fire alight on top, to indicate to mariners in from sea the entrance to the port. The land is flat there and landfall difficult. The Nile pushes its silt well out to sea, and a man-made mark was of great value to ships coming in there.

To the more affluent Arabs, the Egyptians, the Sumerians, the Chaldeans, the Indians, it seems that ocean seafaring was a risky and low-caste calling, left, if possible, to others. Apart from the master class and the wandering merchants who voyaged with their goods, seamen were coolies, slaves. Not for nothing had the Egyptian priesthood set its learned face against the sea. The prophet Mohammed himself left the ruling that "he who twice embarks on the sea is truly an infidel." The

Prophet was a landsman used to camels, but his word was law in the Islamic world.

Even in the big dhow I sailed in during 1938–1939, the same thing applied. Some of the seamen were former slaves, one or two still in slavery. Others were Persian coolies from the bazaar of Kuwait. When at last we sailed into their home port, many had no homes there or anywhere else; they slept in their cloaks in the corners of the bazaar. Within days they went off to the pearling or sailed in the local water dhows, running for river water to the Shatt-al-Arab to earn something to eat.

Such was the tradition of sailing eastern seas and early Mediterranean. The Northmen called Vikings were cast in a very different mold, for they were proud and virile men who could build, man, sail, and fight their own ships for themselves, without an ascetic land-bound priesthood to deter them. They worshiped wild gods like themselves, who approved of sea raids and fighting.

When they swept down from their misty, stormy home waters at the top of the world they cut down the others like a scythe through ripe corn—for a while.

Chapter 7 • **THE VIKINGS**

NORWAY IS A HARD, HIGH LAND. ONLY THE GULF STREAM drift wandering from the Atlantic over the German Sea and along its wild coast makes the place habitable at all to any but Lapps and Eskimos. What land there is can produce little in the brief summers. Indentations and majestic inlets called fiords running deep into the coastal mountains, an inland waterway along much of the west coast, the protection of off-shore islands such as the Lofoten group against the winter storms, offered what the grim land did not—the chance of communications, a reasonable highway by sea.

To use this highway, seaworthy craft had to be developed, and fast. To use these safely, the Norsemen had to be seamen of a high order. This they were. For them seafaring could be no low-caste calling left to underdogs with no future on the land, nor would ships suffice which could sail only in established trades with reliable seasonal winds. They had little trade save the fish from the sea, and the only seasonal winds they knew were storms.

Their greatest leaders were their best seamen. To raid successfully by sea was considered the qualification of full manhood. Rough, tough and arrogant, savagely effective with their long, low ships, they came skimming in from sea upon defenseless Scottish, English, and Irish shores, fell upon the peaceful natives with fire and sword. Before the end of the eighth century, Viking fleets were burning the coastal monasteries of the east coast of England, murdering the monks, and carrying off the treasure. From Weymouth in the English Channel right around the whole east and north coasts, through the Western Isles of Scotland and into Ireland they raided, pillaged, enslaved, and slew.

They had good ships and plenty of them, since these were their principal—often their only—possessions. Other peoples in kinder lands had no ships fit to stand up to them. They sailed into estuaries and far up rivers, for their piratical craft had also the advantage of shallow draft. At times they overran much of Ireland, stormed up the Seine to the city of Paris, seized—and kept—whole provinces of France where Normandy is still known by their name—the land of the Normans, the wild Northmen. The east winds of spring brought them over the German and North seas to ravage the coastal lands of Britain. Soon they spread farther to the south, to Spain and the Mediterranean.

The secret of their success was not just their efficient ruthlessness, but their use of sea power. They were the only nation (if they could be called a nation) with effective sea-going ships. They had no trade and little harvest to bother them. They alone could concentrate sea power and they knew how to use it.

Their ships were not fighting ships in the modern sense. They were ships to transport fighters who carried on war on land. Sixty to eighty feet long, narrow in the beam and shallow in the hold, they were long open boats; but they were lived in, not on, as canoes and log-rafts are. One high mast carrying one large square sail on a wooden yard slung across the vessel gave them motive power; they could also be rowed by their own warriors, seated each on a thwart with a short oar thrust through the ship's side with a leather cup on the hole to keep the water out. No long, unwieldy sweep was used by them. The warriors were their own oarsmen.

Their shipmasters were wild flaxen-haired jarls who swung two-handed battle-axes and sometimes ran along their oars outboard from stem to stern for the sheer devilment of it, while the long ships rolled and sped across the sea. They went berserk at the drop of a bull-horned helmet: some of them seem to have been born berserk, which means blood-red and murdering mad. Fleets of them sped into the Mediterranean in the ninth century. They seized all Sicily, sailed into the Black Sea, took the Russian cities of Novgorod and Kiev. The fearsome figureheads carved at their lofty prows were known and feared even at Byzantium, then capital of the Greek empire.

They could assemble enormous fleets at a time when others could not. Mediterranean galleys could not chase them. The war fleets of such galleys were usually hauled out ashore. It took time to mobilize their crews and get the galleys in the water. The Vikings gave no one time.

It was recorded that, in the year 851, a fleet of 350 Viking ships lay anchored in the Thames. By then they had overrun almost all England. A Viking was king of Dublin. Vikings ruled Brittany and Normandy in France. Vikings from Denmark as well as Norway had made swift and terrible victories in the far-off Mediterranean.

By this period, they were not content with merely raiding. They took over good lands and settled down. Oddly enough, when they ceased murder and took good lands they made these lands better, for these fierce and somewhat individualistic fellows had a genius for good government when they got together. Self-help, a deep sense of order and justice, a real ability to organize on a communal basis were qualities which they possessed, as well as a wild delight in fighting. Within a century of making a success of Normandy they were coming from that land to take over the whole of Britain, this time on a permanent and orderly basis. The ships that the Norman William the Conqueror used in the year 1066 to bring his armies and his horses, his prefabricated fortress for the beach at Pevensy, his fodder and his armor, were modified Viking ships. He did so well that the kingdom he created has never been successfully invaded since.

The Vikings, as every schoolboy is supposed to know until the question comes up at examination time, are acknowledged as the first conquerors of the North Atlantic. With their clinker-built long-boats they sailed from Norway first to Iceland (where the Irish had preceded them with even more remarkable vessels, the skin-hulled, lithe-framed *curraghs* of Ireland). Then, colonizing Iceland, they pushed on toward the West, found Greenland, swept with a favoring current around Cape Farewell and northward to the strait now called Davis, made settlements ashore, moved on to the lands now known as Labrador, Newfoundland, Nova Scotia—perhaps even as far as the coast of what is now New England.

They did all this without compass, charts, or real knowledge of ocean navigation. They did it in open boats offering scant shelter; and on these voyages, for once, there was no rich booty, no one to raid, no luscious fields waiting to be taken over. They had to carve out what they could for themselves. Icelandic, West Greenland's, Newfoundland's, and Nova Scotian waters were rich in fish—fat cod and haddock on the offshore banks, succulent salmon in the streams. But there were fish enough in Norway. Newfoundland and Nova Scotia were rich in soft woods, but so was Norway.

Whatever they may have achieved temporarily on whatever parts of the coast of North America they may have known— and there is considerable controversy still about all this—the Vikings soon gave up. They added nothing to the maps, little

Viking ship preserved in the Folk Museum, Bygdoy, Norway

(at any rate from those voyages) to man's knowledge of the
sea and voyages of discovery.

No Norseman stayed in North America. Within a few years,
the only tradition of their voyaging was in the Icelandic sagas.
These sagas are vague, contradictory, poor evidence. In time,
they gave up their settlements in Greenland, though this large
ice-covered island is still Scandinavian, now under the Danish
flag. The reason may have been because of the very hard win-
ters there, where the absence of anything like a Gulf Stream
drift means savage cold. Latitude for latitude, the weather on
the American side of the Atlantic is much, much colder than
on the European, until one gets well out of the influence of the
Labrador current—a south-going arctic stream—and into the
warm waters of the Gulf Stream, south of the Hudson River.
The Greenland coast is made inaccessible by arctic ice. The
Norwegian is not.

There are some authorities who dispute the fact that transatlantic Viking voyages were ever made. In truth they are
feasible enough. To begin with, the distances are not great,
and at certain seasons of the year the conditions are quite
favorable. We are all so brainwashed with the misleading Mercator's charts from early childhood that most of us have an entirely wrong idea of the extent of northern seas. The Mercator's
projection is a mapmaker's convenience, but often a source of
lifelong inconvenience to the miseducated young. Greenland,
for instance, is made to appear as large almost as all South
America, merely because the sphere being flattened spreads
widest at top and bottom and Greenland is near the top.

The resultant distortion shows the sea distance from Norway's coast to Iceland's to be, apparently, as far as from West
Africa to the tip of Brazil—some sixteen hundred miles. In fact,
it is four hundred, with the Faeroes Islands as a convenient halfway mark. From Iceland's west coast to Greenland's east is

about two hundred miles. Norwegian Vikings maintained communications between the motherland and the west coast of Greenland from the year 985, we are told, for many years.

From west Greenland to the coast of Canada is another comparatively short hop, no matter what the Mercator's atlas might appear to show. In those high northern latitudes there is often a preponderance of easterly winds, especially in the spring. This meant that vessels with a large square sail could then sail west with comparative ease. The Viking vessels had never the weatherly qualities of a big Arab dhow. Their rig was too unhandy and their heavy sails, slung from one yard across the ship and not along its length (as the Arabs and Indians are), could not pull their shallow hulls into the wind. Vikings really did need the favoring winds in the manner that Hippalus and others imagined the Semitic seamen did.

We have plenty of evidence about Viking ships. Several still exist. The Norsemen thought so highly of them that they sometimes buried them, full of equipment and household goods, when their great jarls died. Many such craft disintegrated, but at least two great ships were put down in a kind of clay which preserved them very well. They are now kept indoors in a museum on the Oslo Fjord quite close to the Norwegian capital.

Known as the Gokstad and the Oseberg ships, they are striking vessels. Standing alone in great halls, the first remarkable thing about them is their size, and then the hull-form with its sure harmony of line, its built-in sea-kindliness, its maximum of room on minimum dimensions. With no thought either to cargo stowage or ornate cabins for rich passengers, they are all ship and nothing but ship, seaworthy, swift vessels, contrived to survive in stormy seas. Beam gives them stability, grace gives speed, form gives strength and seaworthiness.

The Oseberg ship is seventy-one feet six inches long with a

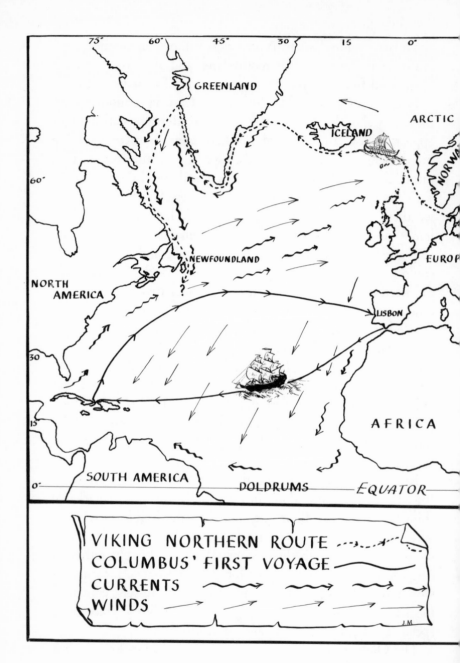

75° 60° 45° 30° 15° 0°

GREENLAND

ICELAND

ARCTIC

NORWAY

60°

EUROPE

NEWFOUNDLAND

NORTH
AMERICA

LISBON

30°

15°

AFRICA

0°

SOUTH AMERICA

DOLDRUMS   EQUATOR

VIKING NORTHERN ROUTE
COLUMBUS' FIRST VOYAGE
CURRENTS
WINDS

J.M.

beam of seventeen feet, a long open boat with thwarts but no
decks, the bows greatly flared and prow and stern built up, the
bow-head surmounted by a ferocious carving. Rude cooking
facilities consist mainly of a cauldron over an open fire. They
steer by "steer-boards," stout oars attached to the starboard quarter with a lever by which the master and his henchman could
twist the blade to direct the water flow across or past it and so
by leverage affect the direction of the ship—steer her, in short.
From such steering oars the evolution of the stern rudder must
have been simple.

The qualities of this Gokstad ship have been well demon-
strated in the sea. A replica, built at Sandefjord in southern
Norway, was sailed from Norway to America in 1893 and made
the voyage comfortably. The vessel sailed from Bergen at the
end of April 1893, bound for the great exposition at Chicago to
mark the four-hundredth anniversary of Columbus' discovery
of America. The Norwegians, thinking perhaps that it was no
harm to remind Americans that the great Italian had had predecessors on the transatlantic run, built the vessel with the utmost care and no modern improvements and sent a master
mariner named Magnus Andersen in command.

The voyage to Newfoundland took four weeks. There was a
lot of bad weather but the replica Gokstad ship sailed and be-
haved well. Captain Andersen and his crew noticed some
rather odd things about her. The bottom planking, for instance,
was tied to the frames with primitive lashings of withy (like
thongs from tough creeper) and nothing else. When the vessel
was laboring in a big seaway, jumping and pitching and heaving and rolling, this bottom gave, like the blubbery coating of a
whale. It was not rigid, as ships' hulls have been for centuries.
It worked up and down as a whale's skin might, but it remained
strong and of one piece, not leaking. It never broke. Not only
the bottom but the whole ship had this capacity for "working":

sometimes the upper planking and half the gunwale could be seen twisted half a foot or so out of true. This elasticity, though surprising to modern seamen, seemed to add both to the ship's strength and speed. She could do ten or eleven knots, and the steering-oar arrangement was most effective.

After the fair in Chicago, the Viking ship was presented to the Field Museum. In an excellent state of preservation, it still stands in a shelter in Chicago's Lincoln Park.

On such long voyages, the Vikings found their way roughly by the sun and the stars, the movements of migratory birds, the scend of the seas before the easterly winds. Easterly weather in the North Atlantic usually lasts for several weeks. (My old Welsh mate in the schoolship *Warspite*, sailing out of Aberdovey in the early 1950's, used always to say when we had east wind, "If we get three days we will get three weeks"—he was usually right.) It is clear then, generally; the stars shine brightly, and the Pole Star was one of several useful guides. If a period of unseemly westerlies set in, of course the Vikings were in trouble. But they could run back for Norway, if they were lost. Heading east before west winds they were bound to come upon their own long coastline somewhere, just as heading west with the east winds they could scarcely miss the high lands of Iceland and Greenland.

The Viking ships, building up no rich trade, setting up no permanent commerce, colonizing nothing but a few grim arctic spots, did their work and then were gone. They were satisfactory for the immediate purposes of the virile, hardy men who sailed them. But they sailed only the coasts of northwest Europe, the summer seas of the Mediterranean, and occasionally at the proper season over at least some part of the Atlantic Ocean. Their major contribution was perhaps to stimulate other nations into a real sea-mindedness, to make others develop better ships with which man might at last really undertake oceanic voyages lasting a hundred days and more, out of sight of land.

Ocean-going ships did not develop from the Viking vessels which, like eastern dhows and Mediterranean galleys, were sufficient for their purpose—just that, and nothing more. The Viking contribution in the use of ocean winds was to show that the easterlies of North Atlantic anticyclones could drive ships a long way, at the right season—just that, and nothing more. The discovery and understanding of the ocean's trade-wind systems and great circulatory currents had to wait for sober and more able men who did not go berserk at all and were not content with piracy, murder, and raiding.

By the early fifteenth century such men existed, and were on the job.

They were the Portuguese. This time they went ahead on sound lines, and the results were splendid and permanent.

Chapter 8 • SEA SENSE FROM PORTUGAL

PORTUGAL IS NOT A MEDITERRANEAN COUNTRY. THE WHOLE of its coastline is in the Atlantic, where winter storms rage upon the beaches, beat upon the bars at the great river mouths, send the salt spray stinging high over cliffs and headlands. In the summers, the north wind blows down from Finisterre to Cape Saint Vincent and the Point of Sagres, an invitation to seamen to spread their sails before it and bound away toward the south. In the summer, too, the sea is quiet along the lovely coast of the southern province called the Algarve, and all these waters then become a glorious cruising ground.

The old ports of the coast of southern Portugal—Lagos, Faro—are sheltered and safe even through the winter months. Down to Portugal's west coast flow several of the greatest rivers from Spain, providing at their mouths useful ports like Oporto, Aveiro, Figueira da Foz, and Lisbon. From their Atlantic beaches Portuguese fishermen have put to sea for thousands of years in quest of fish, and some of the vessels which they use today from places like pretty Nazaré and Costa Nova still bear the same hull forms, still operate in the same way.

The great, sixty-feet long, beamy, and flat-bottomed *barcos-do-mar* which are launched through the surf from half-a-dozen shelving beaches have been in use since Phoenician times. There is Phoenician blood in the veins of many of these fishermen. At a place called Povoa de Varzim, north of Oporto, some

86

of them still use a language of their own and govern themselves by local, ancient ways.

I have put out in these great, high-prowed fishing craft from the Atlantic beaches of Portugal, going with half the village out to sea. First all the village and its bullocks help to get the boat through the first of the surf, then afloat on a great roller. The sweeps, cut from tall trees, are all flailing, flailing—six or eight huge dark men to each. Rising in a smashing of furious broken water, they drop to thump upon the sand and rise again as another nasty roller flings itself violently in and the sweeps flash wet and bending with the wild effort of the fishermen.

Ahead is the tall stempost like that in Phoenician and Viking ships, surmounted not by a pagan figurehead but by a bunch of flowers. Over the stern a long, hand-twisted rope is payed out, and, as the graceful craft gets beyond the surf and out to sea, a huge net follows this line, buoyed with blown-up hogs' bladders weighted on the bottom with pieces of lead.

The oxen will not go into the surf; they help only as far as the water's edge. Men must get the vessel properly sea-borne. The effort is immense but perfectly organized. Out they go some miles to sea, then turn and run along the coast putting out

Bullocks and men help to haul the high-prowed fishing craft ashore at Nazaré, Portugal.

Alan Villiers

their net; at the net's end they run in for the beach, bringing back the long rope. Again they come in through the surf with maximum care and ordered cooperation. The great craft pitches, leaps, and thumps its fat flat bottom down. It must, above all, be held quite straight lest the breaking surf cause it to swing broadside on, out of control, overwhelm it, turn it over, spill out the forty men and, falling on them, smash them down in the sea within sight of their homes. Oxen stand ready by the surf's edge to pick up the line from the net and begin to haul in, while others strain at ropes swiftly attached to the prow. Out leap the fishermen.

Men and oxen combine for a few frantic moments at the mighty effort of getting the craft clear of the surf, women and children flinging pine-tree rollers underneath it to lighten the task, wet through, straining. Once clear of the sea the oxen swing the craft prow outward again, ready for the next launching as soon as a fresh net is loaded. The fishermen get on at once with the task of stowing this net quickly and skillfully, to be sure that it will pay out clear.

Such fishermen must be brave, strong, and fearless seamen. They live on bread, fish, vegetables, olive oil, and wine, as they always have. They ask little, give much, for the return from coastal fishing is often poor. They follow a way of life handed down to them through countless generations. All sea fishing is hard, and this is but one of the methods used in Portugal. No wonder, then, that when fearless seamen were needed for dangerous, open-sea, pioneering voyages, Portugal had them at hand. To such men, regular watch-keeping and regular meals aboard a sea-going caravel would be a pleasant change, even if she were bound for the ends of the earth.

At first, Portuguese fishing and seafaring were coasting, though in the North Atlantic. The inspiration that brought about their change to ocean voyaging came from a landsman, the great prince named Henry, called, later, The Navigator, though he never navigated a ship at sea in his life.

Henry the Navigator, half English, half Portuguese (his mother was a daughter of the English John of Gaunt), was born at Oporto in 1394. Early in his life he led a successful foray against the Moors (the Moslem Arabs) at the fortress of Ceuta guarding one side of the entrance to the Mediterranean. Later, still youthful, he went on another military expedition not so successful. After that he retired to a secluded spot on the Point of Sagres at Portugal's windswept southwestern corner.

Here were no princely pleasures, nor did he seek them. A highly intelligent, reflective man with a scientific turn of mind, Prince Henry henceforward devoted his life to organizing the solution of the ocean's mysteries to allow men to master them and safely make ocean voyages. But more than that, the mariners would be able properly to conduct these voyages from position to position. They would have knowledge enough to fix these positions so that, finding new lands, or new routes to old ones, they could plot the course and chart the land. Knowing precisely where they had been and the way they got there, other men could take ships on similar voyages again and again. Coastal wanderings with seasonal winds would not suffice. Prince Henry faced squarely up to the Atlantic problem, and his farsighted objective was from the first the riches of the East, the trade of India. Was not their control of this the whole basis of the Moors' strength and prosperity? In Prince Henry's day, these Moors seemed on their way to the destruction of all Christian Europe. The source of their power was not just the fanaticism of the new religion of Islam. They had wealth, too—tremendous wealth. And this was based upon the monopolistic control of the rich trade which originated thousands of miles away, in India.

Prince Henry knew of this. He had his own agents and informants; Greeks and Romans had been there long ago. Merchants of the great city-states of Italy knew at least some of the spice trade secrets, for they profited from a similar monopolistic control of the distributing end in Europe.

To begin with, Henry the Navigator had the seamen and the ports.

He had little else. No one knew, for instance, how far the summer north wind blew once it had passed Portugal. No one knew the Atlantic currents or oceanic winds. There was a tradition of one Phoenician voyage around the south of Africa centuries before, but, apart from the reference in Herodotus, it was only a tradition. There was that reference in the *Periplus* to the meeting of the seas south of Africa. The Prince conceived the idea early that he would have to find the way around Africa, and the first step was to assemble all the learned men he could find and induce to visit his establishment at Sagres. There, for the sake of further enlightenment, they would pool such knowledge as they had. They would think and talk over the theories put forward by the Greeks and others, work upon a basis of Semitic mathematics and astronomy in order to establish (if it could be done) some certain means for fixing the positions of ships crossing the trackless sea, and then devise instruments which would provide accurate data for this purpose.

All this was a big order. But these fifteenth-century "backroom boys" were in no hurry. They drew no attention to themselves. They publicized nothing. Italians, Arabs, Jews, a Spaniard from Majorca worked quietly together with the Portuguese in their crude observatory there on the windswept point. Pilots with their specialized knowledge, cartographers and compass makers, seamen who commanded ships in the Mediterranean and on northern voyages were called in.

In those days, such ships were steered and piloted with pains-

Prince Henry the Navigator

National Maritime Museum, Greenwich, England

taking care. When they had to leave the land to cross a hundred miles or so of open water before picking up the next piece of land the ship's reckoning was kept as exactly as possible so that it would always be known how far she had gone.

They kept a mariner's compass set always against the mast, besides another on the poop by which a lantern burned all night; and when they were at sea they never took their eyes off this latter. There was always someone watching it, and from time to time he sang out sweetly and melodiously, an indication that the voyage was going melodiously [and also that he was awake].*

Pilots were highly skilled specialists who owned their own charts and had personally acquired from long study and experience the knowledge they possessed. They had a good knowledge of contemporary sailing-ships' speeds, though they lacked precise means of measuring them. The watchman kept the ship's reckoning by means of a peg board set out with colored pegs on strings, which he had only to move from hole to hole.** Only the pilot need be literate. These ships, too, balanced and steered well, as all native craft did and still do. It was useless in the days of sail to launch an ill-balanced, bad-steering thing to waddle off-course and bewilder helmsman and pilot alike. (That sort of ship had to wait for the steam age.)

All this was very well, but it would not do for the long run to India. The true foundation of navigation must be mathematics based on sufficient knowledge of astronomy. The ancient Semitic peoples had made wonderful strides in both these sciences,

* The description, by Brother Felix, of a passage in the Mediterranean in 1483, quoted by Commander D. W. Waters R.N.
** We used this when sailing the replica of the sixteenth-century bark *Mayflower* to America in 1957. It was foolproof and worked very well.

as the precise planning of their cities and monuments still testi-
fies. (In the Great Pyramid of Khufu dating to around 3000
B.C., for instance, a shaft is so arranged that the rays of the star
Sirius shine directly into it, and upon the tomb of the Pharaoh,
at its every transit of the meridian.)

The problem now was to assemble all this knowledge and
to convert it to sea use. Men knew, for instance, how to establish latitude by measuring at noon the angular distance north or
south of the sun. They had instruments for this purpose. But
how to convert these instruments for use from the heeling decks
of a little ship, pitching and rolling in the sea? That was one
problem. Another was to devise tables which could show far
ahead just what was the sun's declination—the spot on earth
where it was precisely overhead—at any time. It was of no use
to be able to measure the sun's noon altitude if the navigator
did not also know for certain just where the sun was.

So instruments, tables, better charts must all be devised, and
seamen instructed in their use.

There must also be better *ships*, stronger, larger ships, but
still well balanced, able to sail on a wind as well as before one.
By this time, northern Europe's seamen had worked out a
simple three-masted ship with a rig based on one large mast
more or less in the center—the mainmast—and two others, one
well forward—the foremast—and the other aft—the mizzen.
Ahead was rigged a spar to jut well out in front of the ship.
From this a smaller sail was set, a spritsail, as it was called. Being so far forward this sail was valuable both for swinging the
ship when necessary and for balancing her. Its windage offset
the force of the wind on the big after-castle which was built
up over the poop, first to provide a platform for the fighting
men and later to accommodate them and the richer passengers
as well.

This sort of ship developed in time into the modern full-rigged ship (such as the *Joseph Conrad* at Mystic, the *Constitution* in Boston Navy Yard, the *Cutty Sark* at Greenwich, H.M.S. *Victory* in Portsmouth Dockyard). Such ships were cumbersome for exploratory voyages. They required fairly large crews, and could not sail very close to the direction of the wind. This meant that in adverse conditions they could be blown off the land. Nor were Mediterranean galleys any better. The disqualifications of their enormous crews, their long, weaker hulls, and the necessity for frequent beaching ruled them out altogether.

But why not a combination of the two types? A small but seaworthy hull carrying a rig which combined the lateen of the galleys and the square sail of the ship? Such a vessel would be safe, fast, and weatherly.

So the famous Portuguese caravel was born. Some caravels were small with a purely lateen rig on two or three masts. Others were larger with the combination of a big square sail or two on the foremast, and two or three other masts each with a lateen.

All this development took time. Seamen do not approve of rapid change. Meanwhile, the prince began his program of exploratory voyages by sending small caravels and other vessels on probing voyages before the north wind, along the coast of Africa. From knowledge of the great African caravan routes, he had an idea of what might be found at least for the first thousand miles. Semitic camel trains had been trading from time immemorial from great bases in Egypt, westward toward the market places of the coast, eastward to Kosseir and Suakin, the ancient ports of the Red Sea. What the Semitic traders could achieve by land the Portuguese seamen could do by sea, better.

But the way proved painfully difficult. Courtiers led the small expeditions, in vessels which nowadays would scarcely suffice to lighter a little cargo in a sheltered port. Courtiers were the leaders because that was their function. They were not seamen, but their whole purpose was to lead whatever and wherever the court might require them. They were born, reared, and trained to lead as a right and duty. Courtiers were educated, seamen not. Seamen did the sailing, but the chosen knights and *fidalgos* had command. Nor were these voyages for private enterprise. They were for Portugal, ordained by royal policy. Therefore men chosen by the royal prince must lead them.

There were times when this did not work out very well. It was perhaps one thing to come before the royal presence, suitably and magnificently attired, to receive the grand instructions. It could be quite another when, off the hot coast of Africa, the seamen began to murmur of boiling water further south, of a torrid zone where no man could live, of strange beasts and enormous fish waiting in the sea to gobble them all up, then perhaps to overwhelm the ship and sink her without a trace.

Voyage after voyage found little. The path of discovery was slow, difficult, sometimes heartbreaking for the courtiers and the prince who sent them. It took fifteen years to feel a way past the first important headland, Cape Bojador, just south of the Canary Islands, and another twenty years after that to grope as far as Cape Verde.

> Said the mariners, this much we know, that beyond this Cape of Bojador there is no race of men or place of inhabitants; nor is the land less sandy than the deserts of Libya, where there is no water, no green tree, no green herb—and the sea so shallow that a whole league from the land it is only six feet deep, while the currents are so terrible that a ship, once having passed the Cape, will never be able to return.*

* Recorded by the Portuguese historian Azurara.

That is what frightened them, the fearful prospect of being unable to return. The better were the means of southward sailing the harder must be the return; for they would first have to get away from the land, to get sea room before they could fight back against the north wind. And that north wind seemed to blow on forever, and the current set south with it, at the rate of knots.

Working back for Portugal, they found the island of Madeira first, then the Azores, which were well out in the Atlantic. Neither group showed signs of habitation, which was strange, for these are lovely islands. Driving southward they came at length upon the Cape Verde Islands, also without people.

Year after year the quest went on. The courtiers and the captains came in due course upon market towns on the coast of Africa where they could trade for slaves, ivory, sometimes a little gold. Some settled for this, hurrying back to reap a profit. Nor could they be blamed. There was such an enormous lot of Africa. When would it ever end? Past Guinea, down the Ivory Coast and the Gold Coast, past the great rivers known now as the Senegal, Niger, and Congo, they felt their way along— and at length around all the vast bulge of west Africa—only to find the land stretching forever in their way, seemingly without end. The noble prince died in 1460 with his first quest still unfinished.

Down into the South Atlantic his ships continued to sail, the North Atlantic already behind them. The Portuguese seamen had by then worked out quite well how to sail efficiently home to Portugal after running down with the north and northeast winds. They stood out to sea and took the wind over their right side, which blew them on a northwesterly course toward the Azores or Madeira, if they were lucky, and kept them out of the south-going current.

So knowledge of ocean voyaging slowly improved. Passages

homeward across the open sea, which once seamen would have feared like the plague, became accepted as a matter of course.

Still the vast hot mainland of Africa stretched southward. The Portuguese were beyond the Equator now, and knew well that no boiling sea was there, or anywhere else. But they had sailed far past the zone of the northerly winds. Now the winds came steadily the other way, in their faces. They groped along, making a way wearily with offshore land breezes by night and onshore sea breezes by day. With both they could sail south with the wind abeam—on their left by night, on their right by day.

The further south they went the worse the coast became, which provided sufficient real hazards and dangers to make up for the imaginary ones.

Worse, the land and sea breezes were unreliable. It dawned upon someone at last that the only way to find the extremity of land was to leave the land altogether, take the persistent southeast wind upon the ship's left side and let her go. Let her blow offshore, let her lose sight of the accursed land, let her sail the wide ocean where no man had sailed before! The southeast wind must come to an end some time. It was reasonable then to expect, sooner or later, a system of countering westerlies.

So said the sages at Sagres, where the work the great prince had started lived after him.

As in so much of sea history, there is no real certainty who first tried out this new idea. He was a very brave man, for the latitude of the end of Africa was still unknown and neither then nor for some centuries afterward could navigators establish longitude. The pioneer could be swallowed up in the abyss of the tremendous sea, sail his ship out of water and provisions, die alone and miserably with nothing achieved.

An obscure seafarer, by name Bartolomeo Diaz—called Bartholomeu Dias in the English-language histories—at last sailed

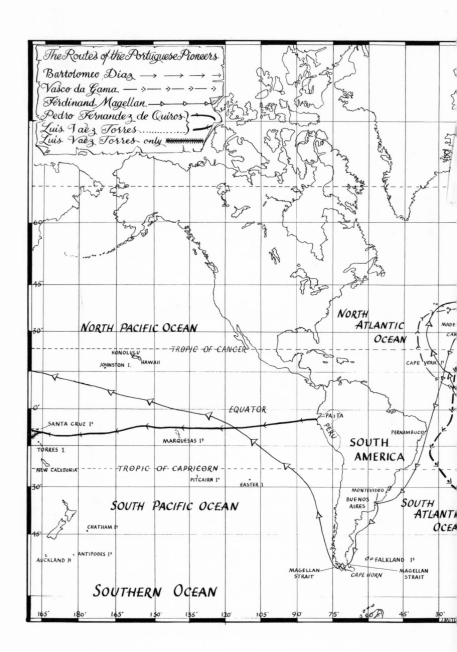

The Routes of the Portuguese Pioneers

Bartolomeo Diaz → → → →
Vasco da Gama, —→—→—→—→
Ferdinand Magellan—▷ ▷ ▷
Pedro Fernandez de Quiros⟩
Luis Vaèz Torres..............⟩
Luis Vaèz Torres only ➤➤➤➤➤

NORTH PACIFIC OCEAN

NORTH ATLANTIC OCEAN

MADE
CA

TROPIC OF CANCER
CAPE VERDE I⁵
HONOLULU
JOHNSTON I.   HAWAII

EQUATOR
PAITA

SANTA CRUZ I⁵
PERNAMBUCO
MARQUESAS I⁵
TORRES I.
PERU
SOUTH AMERICA

NEW CALEDONIA   TROPIC OF CAPRICORN
PITCAIRN I⁵   EASTER I
MONTEVIDEO
BUENOS AIRES
SOUTH ATLANTI OCEA

SOUTH PACIFIC OCEAN
CHATHAM I⁵

AUCKLAND I⁵   ANTIPODES I⁵
FALKLAND I⁵
MAGELLAN STRAIT   CAPE HORN   MAGELLAN STRAIT

SOUTHERN OCEAN

165° 180° 165° 150° 135° 120° 105° 90° 75° 60° 45° 30°

J.MIT

98

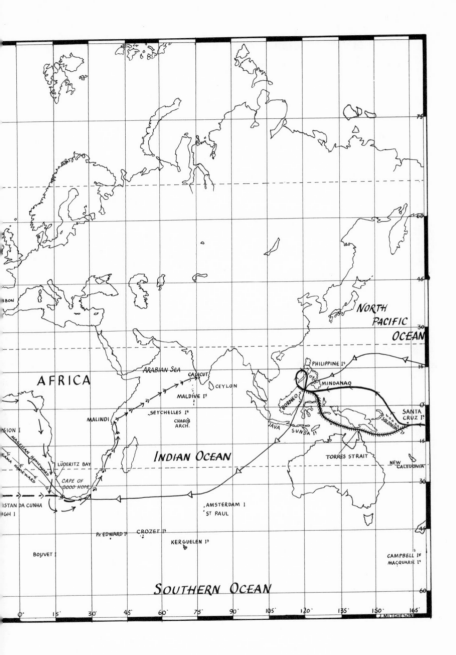

NORTH
PACIFIC
OCEAN

AFRICA

ARABIAN SEA

CALICUT

CEYLON

MALDIVE Iˢ

SEYCHELLES Iˢ

CHAGOS
ARCH.

PHILIPPINE Iˢ

MINDANAO

BORNEO

SANTA
CRUZ Iˢ

SOLOMON Iˢ

MALINDI

JAVA

SUNDA Iˢ

LÜDERITZ BAY

CAPE OF
GOOD HOPE

INDIAN OCEAN

TORRES STRAIT

NEW
CALEDONIA

AMSTERDAM I
ST PAUL

TISTAN DA CUNHA

Pʳ EDWARD Iˢ

CROZET Iˢ

KERGUELEN Iˢ

BOUVET I

CAMPBELL Iˢ
MACQUARIE Iˢ

SOUTHERN OCEAN

0°   15°   30°   45°   60°   75°   90°   105°   120°   135°   150°   165°

south of Africa. Blown away, it was said, from the mainland of
Africa for many days, at length he stood back with the westerly
winds, as forecast; he allowed his little ship to run on before
them for several days. He saw no land, nothing but huge seas
everywhere.

After allowing what he considered good time to pass all the
southern tip of Africa—for it was obvious now that he *was*
south of all the land—he swung to the north again, now with
the wind on his left side, his ship's port beam. He trimmed
the sails of his caravel on this new course and stood northward, all hands with their eyes peeled, keeping sharp lookout
for first glimpse of the expected land—the first seamen since
the Phoenicians to see Africa from the south.

It was stormy weather, but the caravel rode well.

The seamen began to mutter at all this open-sea voyaging.
It was cold, wet, stormy. They had been out a long, long time
—longer than any previous ships had been.

At last Diaz made landfall at Mossel Bay. He was past the
cape, in the Indian Ocean. The further route to long-sought
India lay open before him. Triumph at last! But Diaz was
robbed of it.

The seamen would not go on. Turn back now for home
again, they said, or we mutiny.

They meant it. They had the whip hand. And what they
said was true; they had achieved a great thing and had tidings
enough to bring cheer to the Court, without undertaking also
the further long and hazardous run to the coasts of India.

Diaz turned back, sailed safely to Portugal, came into the
Tagus at length with pennants flying, drums going, trumpets
blaring. The year was 1487 or 1488—no one seems quite sure
which.

Among those standing by the Tagus banks to welcome Diaz
from Good Hope was an obscure Genoese named Columbus,

a sort of seaman and cartographer, an odd fellow who seemed obsessed with some very curious ideas about voyages even more strange than this just made by Diaz.

Diaz was not given the honor of following up his epochal discovery. Within a decade he was dead, drowned in a storm in the South Atlantic while on a voyage to Brazil with his countryman Cabral.

Within that same decade, at last, the plans of Henry the Navigator burst into full reality. In a few brief years, the Western world was to see voyages made successfully which hitherto only men thought mad had dreamed of, a veritable explosion of discovery by the wonderful routes through the sea.

Chapter 9 • **THE SCIENCE OF OCEAN VOYAGING**

Within ten years of the return of Bartolomeo Diaz from his discovery of the Cape of Good Hope, the Portuguese Vasco da Gama was making his wonderful twenty-four-thousand-mile voyage from the Tagus at Lisbon to Calicut in India, and back again—the most wonderful sea voyage that had been made to that time. Another Portuguese named Pedro Alvares Cabral had put South America on the map. The most extraordinary of them all, the Genoese-born, Spanish-domiciled Christopher Columbus, had driven westward before the northeast trade winds of the North Atlantic, and, stumbling upon the West Indies, declared that he had found the East. In fact he had opened the way to the Americas. After Da Gama, Portuguese fleets began regular voyages to the riches of the East. The Portuguese spread from India to the Persian Gulf, the Malay Archipelago, and to China and Japan.

In this same period yet another Portuguese, Ferdinand Magellan, worked a fleet of small ships from Europe through the length of the South Atlantic on its western side and fought his way through the stormy straits which still bear his name, and sailed then across the whole breadth of the enormous Pacific, an ocean so tremendous that it alone accounts for half the water in the world.

Not content with that and with achieving the aim of the Greek philosophers of reaching the East by sailing west, some of his men and one of his ships continued through the East

102

Ferdinand
Magellan

National Maritime Museum, Greenwich, England

Indies, across the whole of the Indian Ocean and around Good
Hope from east to west, through both Atlantics, and back to
Spain.

Here were three marvelous voyages in one colossal achievement, any of which would have been utterly impossible a short
score of years before—from Spain to the Pacific by the Strait
of Magellan, from the tip of Chile to the Spice Islands and the
Philippines (this alone was stupendous and marvelous, the
longest nonstop voyage ships had ever made)—and, on top of
all this, the first circumnavigation.

When at last he entered the waters of the sea misnamed
Pacific after fighting his way through the Strait of Magellan,
itself a piece of sailing so tough that all the modern sailing

ships avoided it, preferring the open seas off Cape Horn, Magellan had no idea of the prodigious effort which still lay before his little ships and his hard-working crews. Neither he nor anyone on earth had an inkling then of the real immensity of this sea against which, for the first time in man's history, he was cheerfully pitting a few cockleshell ships. Already they were too long out from base. They had not the slightest prospect of replenishing anything until they might return again a year or so later, if ever.

His heart light with the passage of the grim and stormy straits behind him, Magellan set his ships' heads toward the northwest first, to get into better weather and away from the frigid neighborhood of Cape Horn. It was a long way to the tropics even if he could sail direct—a tough two thousand miles to their southern edge. But he knew where he was going, and the way was now open.

Magellan had already been to the Spice Islands, coming by the established way around Good Hope and through the Indian Ocean. He knew that he must sail to the correct latitude and then run west. Well, he knew the latitude of the Spice Islands.

Off he set, in good heart, and his crews in good spirits. They sailed out of the gray south into the sunshine again, at last. They picked up, after many days, the soft trade winds of the Pacific in the zone where that ocean really deserves its name. They turned westward and west-northwest and sailed on and on.

Weeks, months later Magellan was still sailing westward, on and on and on! The sea mocked him with the endless repetition of its heartless rim; the wind mocked him, forever blowing him slowly on in the same direction; the blue sea followed, scarred briefly by his wake, and the blue sea stretched forever ahead until it burned his dark eyes to look at it, burned into his brain, and all his men's.

Never as much as the palm tree of a coral island lifted itself from that endless sea as Magellan's ships, crossing at last the most island-studded ocean in the world, missed through some quirk of fate all the islands, all the atolls, all hope of wayside replenishment of any kind. The way of the ocean pioneers was excessively hard, and none harder than Magellan's. Food gave out. The sailors stewed their leather boots, their leather belts and jerkins, the leather chafing gear they cut down from the shrouds, the parrels of the yards. The few remaining barrels of fresh water stank, and a slimy, smelly mess oozed between the staves. There had been plenty of bread, wine, dried fish, and salt meat, and plenty of olive oil to cook the viands with. The royal ovens at Lisbon had worked long hours baking their biscuit; and those ovens could turn out more than a thousand tons a year.

Now the few biscuits left were full of weevils and worm. The wine was sour, the meat all gone, and nearly all the olive oil with it.

Still the little ships sailed forever west and west-northwest, and forever the ocean—so deceptively sunlit and smiling— reached away before them. As the months passed, more and more of the seamen and the soldiers died and were buried in that so falsely smiling sea.

Aloft, the cordage rigging scarcely held the sun-bleached masts together or sufficed to work the yards; the threadbare canvas seemed about to part with every slightest freshening of the wind, for it was worn so thin with the unprecedented long passage that it looked like tissue paper. Nor did their leader have knowledge of either the position of his ships or how far still they might have to go. Neither then nor for almost the next three hundred years could any navigator fix the position of his ship truly in the sea. He knew her latitude, yes—for what that might be worth. But her distance east or west of the land she had left or that to which she tried to sail he could not discover at all. There were no means; he could only keep his "reckoning." . . .

The reckoning in the Magellan flagship reached a staggering total, and still there was no land. The sailors lay about on decks, gums puffed up, swollen and bleeding, teeth falling out, their legs gone useless with the accursed sea disease called scurvy. They began to wish there really was an end to the sea and they would find it—a precipice beyond the horizon where their poor ships would tumble over and go tumbling into eternity, their worries lost in one mad, fatal descent into the abyss of time.

It was not to be. They must sail on.

When at last the long-sought islands came slowly up from the farther rim after nine thousand miles of sea, a grim and pitiful remnant could not raise a cheer.

In fact, the Magellan epic achieved little beyond the knowledge of its intense difficulties. This new way to the islands was scarcely practicable, for there was far too much of the Pacific altogether. It was better to use the other way, the shorter, easier way that Diaz found and Da Gama pioneered.

Magellan never had his triumph. He was killed on a beach in the Philippines in some foolish local fight.

Not many years afterward, Spanish navigators were more or less regularly making two-way voyages between their colonies in eastern seas right across the North Pacific to the west coast of their colonies in America. They sailed east with the Pacific's west winds in high latitudes, back with the favoring trade winds in low. Farther to the south, still another Portuguese, that mystic pilot and Columbus of the South Seas, Ferdinand Queiros, was sailing westward from Peru to the Marquesas and the Solomon Islands, to the New Hebrides and on from there to Manila in the Philippines. His countryman Luis Vaz de

Torres took the discovery of the straits called Torres between northern Australia and eastern New Guinea in his stride, after sailing with Queiros from Peru.

What Queiros and Torres really did was to come upon the fringing islands off Australia, as Columbus had sailed to the fringing islands of the continent of America. But Australia's off-lying islands were far out in the South Seas: the conquest of the sea route to this last continent was by no means the simple matter that the run from Europe to the West Indies and Central America soon became—a downhill sail before the favoring trade winds which, in later years, has been successfully made by a German in a rubber canoe, a Frenchman on a raft, and ten thousand wandering yachtsmen.

This sudden upsurge of magnificent activity in ocean voyaging all stemmed from the pioneering work of Portugal. None of these great voyages was made, or could be made, by chance. What the Portuguese really discovered was the way to make effective use of the ocean system of winds and currents—first in the North Atlantic, then the South Atlantic, then the Indian Ocean beyond the monsoon's area, and, finally, across the South Seas. They were the first to link the seas, to see and use the watery world as what it was—one ocean, one linked and inexhaustible highway for the ships of man.

The first light upon this vast achievement was that thrown somewhat hazily by Diaz. After his voyage, there is a curious wait of ten years before Vasco da Gama is sent off to profit by what Diaz had discovered, but the sailing directions prepared by the court authorities at Lisbon and given to Da Gama could scarcely be bettered for a square-rigged ship today. He was instructed to run south with the *Nortada*—the coastal north wind —and the trades; then, after working his way through the doldrums belt of cats'-paws and wet calms, he was not to try to approach the coast of Africa at all but *to stand boldly right through the zone of the southeast trade winds* where he found them, with the wind on his ship's left side, letting her sail as well as possible without jamming her into the wind.

After that, after having made this great, wide swing toward west and south far out of sight of land, he was to turn eastward to clear the Cape of Good Hope on the appropriate latitude. Here he could expect variable winds and westerlies. Once past Good Hope he could work up the coast of East Africa, as the Arabs did, crossing to the Indian coast from a convenient point. As far as the Atlantic was concerned, these are the same directions which were given to big sailing ships in the twentieth century. All the square-riggers bound out to South Africa, India, the Far East, and Australia sailed that way, for it could not be bettered. True, sometimes ships were forced over to the coast of Brazil when some vagary of the wind brought the trades more from south than east; in this way the coast of Brazil was probably first seen.

The odd thing is—how was the sailing knowledge acquired upon which these directions to Da Gama were based? All that could not be worked out by the "backroom boys." Neither could the knowledge have been gained with such assurance from the one prior voyage of which we have knowledge today. (Wrongly to route so important a fleet as Da Gama's was unthinkable! Yet the directions are concise and definite.)

It is obvious that there must have been many voyages of which no knowledge has come down to us at all, and the Portuguese knew not only this sea road to Good Hope. They were also perfectly aware that the best sailing route to the East *was* by sailing first south by way of the Cape of Good Hope. Columbus and Da Gama sought the same objective, after all; Da Gama found it, while Columbus fetched up upon the impenetrable bar of a whole new continent whose eastern coast was nine thousand miles from his wished-for destination.

Vasco da Gama

There are persistent stories of early transatlantic voyages. There are names on old maps, islands called Brazil and the Antilles which were on Atlantic charts long before Columbus sailed that way. There is a tradition of other Portuguese voyages, of groping toward the northwest passage and coming upon the rich banks of codfish off Newfoundland while trying to find the northern end of this vast, cold, and then useless land. Old maps show Newfoundland itself as "territory of the King of Portugal," "Land of the *Bacalhau*," which is the Portuguese word for cod.

By 1500 and probably long before—indeed, before Columbus —Portugal was sending fishermen across the Atlantic by way of the Azores to the Newfoundland banks, to bring back rich cargoes of salted cod. In the ten years' wait between Diaz and Da Gama, those well-informed backroom boys of Lisbon were checking on the Columbus discovery, making quite sure that, after all, there was no way to India's markets over the Atlantic. It would have been most convenient to them if there was, for Portugal was ideally placed to exploit such a sailing route.

From all this, the Portuguese worked out the way for ships of the day—and after them, all sailing ships—not only to make Indian voyages but also voyages to Brazil, to the Strait of Magellan, to the West Indies, and back again. The pattern of Atlantic winds and currents did not offer the same clear-cut, readily usable monsoon system of eastern seas. But there *was* a pattern, and it *could* be used. Discovering this was far more important and of greater permanent value than the making, by God's grace, of some fortuitous one-way passage. These Iberian pioneers succeeded by hard work over many years; there was nothing fortuitous about them.

In the North Atlantic, taking an over-all view, the sea goes slowly round and round with movements on a wide front, called currents. The surface water drifts from the west to east and back again, with a clockwise motion, coming out of the Gulf of Mexico and swinging up the Atlantic seaboard, thence eastward and north-eastward toward northwest Europe with, as well, a circulatory movement maintained by waters sweeping south-eastward past the Azores and southward off the coast of Portugal. From here, the south-going stream called the Canary Current swings down toward the Cape Verde Islands, then westward as the north Equatorial to become in part the north subtropical—still going west—and in part to flow toward the Gulf of Mexico and replenish the Gulf Stream.

So the ocean's surface water goes round and round and round, rarely at a great rate except sometimes when constricted by the land, as in the straits of Florida. At the same time, the wind system settles itself down into the trades, toward which

The nav (or naõ) of Vasco da Gama—rigged down to her lower-masts at left, under full sail at right.

the *Nortada* of the Portuguese coast is a famous pusher. These trade winds blow in the tropics roughly from north to south, being deflected by the earth's rotation to the east of north in the North Atlantic and the east of south in the South Atlantic. Beyond these to the north is a zone of variables, a nuisance in the days of sail and, beyond these again, toward the latitude of 35 or 40 north, a zone of west winds. Beyond them again, up toward the Vikings' old stamping ground, at certain times of the year there are fairly reliable easterlies.

And so, though there may at times be wide variety even in established winds, it is possible for the master of a square-rigged ship to plan a voyage, say from Portugal to the West Indies and back, going west with the trades and the helpful north subtropical current, and then coming back again by getting first in the Gulf Stream to sweep up to the north, and there picking up the westerlies to blow his ship home.

A very odd thing, indeed, is that this is exactly what Columbus did on his very first voyage, as if he knew the secret of the

Christopher Columbus

North Atlantic as well as Da Gama had been informed of the sailing secrets of the South. The Italian was his own "backroom boy." He had made no previous voyages in those parts; according to him, no one had. How, then, did he know these things if others had not found them out? Not just one predecessor—a whole fleet of them, sailing over years. It was known quite well that driftwood from some land far to the west came up on the beaches of the Azores Islands, and there was a strong tradition of voyages made long ago to *something* out there. But here one speculates, and that is idle.

There is another odd fact about Columbus and his voyages. He seems to have destroyed much of his own notes made before the voyages. At least, they are lost. We have no hope now of finding out what he might have known before he sailed. We do not know the amount of his prior knowledge, if any. He remains the most mysterious navigator of them all. He seems indeed never to have realized just what his voyages had achieved, the bringing of two great new continents to the map of the world. Until the day he died he seemed convinced that he had come upon the fringing islands not of new America but of old Asia, somewhere not far from its fabulous markets with their riches almost beyond the dreams of man.

Poor Columbus! Visionaries are hard to put up with at any time, but when they continue for years to exhort their disillusioned followers to explore and exploit the wrong land, they must be trying indeed. At last Columbus was taken from the West Indies home to his adopted Spain in chains, and there, vociferous and—in a way—wrong to the last, he died.

After the great voyages between 1488 and 1520, European discovery of all the sea-washed lands upon the globe was possible and practicable. With inspired courtiers to lead them, and a few painstaking, courageous, and competent mariners with a handful of white-sailed, small wooden ships, the pioneers of little Portugal had opened the sea ways of the world.

It was a remarkable achievement. For a small country—one of the smallest in all Europe—never before either rich or powerful, with a population that did not exceed one and a half million most of whom were peasants with none but the vaguest idea of what was going on, it was miraculous.

There has remained something miraculous about it. Portuguese and Spanish dominance could not last, though the Pope
divided the globe conveniently between them. Other greedier,
more powerful nations with perhaps more ruthless seamen and,
as time went on, larger and better ships, came sailing after them,
the Dutch and the French and the English. In time these
carved up most of the Iberian overseas settlements and trade
among them, the Dutch and English taking the lion's share,
and developed an ocean-going sailing commerce which grew
and grew. A million and a half could not stand up to twenty
million.

But in the 1960's these empires, too, have faded away.

It is very odd that now again only the Portuguese remain.
Until very recently they were still in India, in their enclaves
of Goa, Damão, and Diu. The Portuguese peoples there, black,
white, and brown, resented the aggression that, after all other
methods had failed, openly seized their territories and made
them part of India. Even today the Portuguese flag flies over
half Timor in Indonesia and all Macão on the mainland of
China, and Madeira and the Azores and the Cape Verde Islands, Angola and Mozambique. Portuguese is the language of
Brazil.

Portuguese place names sprinkle the sea routes of the world
and their surnames are legion in Ceylon, Calcutta, and Pakistan.
Portuguese churches and cathedrals still beautify the hills over
much of Ceylon and parts of India, and are filled with wor-
shipers. Portuguese bronze cannon still stand at the ramparts
of Malé in the Maldive Islands. Portuguese fortresses, built
there by the great Affonso d'Albuquerque, still stand solid upon
the sunburned hills of Muscat, still guard the entrance to the
port of Mombasa, four and a half centuries after a handful of
extraordinary sea-expert people, inspired by a recluse prince and
a deep and abiding sense of destiny, put them there.

Chapter 10 • **THE ENGLISH AND THE DUTCH**

PORTUGUESE SEAMEN PIONEERED THE SEA ROUTES TO INDIA and the Indies by way of the Cape of Good Hope and the Strait of Magellan. After Columbus, in due course there was yet another practical though tedious route. This was to sail across the North Atlantic, in the usual way, to the Isthmus of Panama, using the trade winds and favoring currents, then to land and transport men and goods by mule train to the Pacific side where they could take ship in locally built Spanish vessels either for coastal passages to Peru or Mexico or to sail across the Pacific to the Spice Islands on the other side.

This third route was restricted principally to treasure ships coming up from Peru with gold and silver, and illustrious dons and fighting men traveling between old and new Spain. Magellan's route by his dangerous strait was not really suitable for sailing ships.

But there were other routes. There was a dangerous but quite usable route around the tip of South America, past the headland called Cape Horn. This was first rounded in 1615 by the Dutchman Le Maire and Schouten with a couple of early seventeenth-century cockleshells named the *Concord* and the *Hoorn*. This intrepid pair, who set out to find a new route to the East Indies and so to cut in on the monopoly then held by the Dutch East India Company, had better luck with the westerly winds off the Horn than most of their successors enjoyed,

115

for after finding the place and naming it they had sailed past it and into the Pacific in little over a week.

Off the Horn they found a "great sea," inhabited only by "sea mews, larger than swans, with wings stretching a fathom across" which flew "screaming round the ships." These were the famous albatrosses whose wingspread is not one fathom but two—twelve feet—and often more. This first glimpse of the albatrosses alarmed the mariners, for the wind kicked up from the west and blew a gale with a very high sea, and the spray and spume smashed over the little Dutch vessels. But they persevered.

The government of Holland had offered the rich prize of the profits from four East Indies voyages to any Dutch navigator finding a new route to those fabulous islands. Their East India Company had exclusive rights only for the routes around Good Hope and through the Strait of Magellan. What the government really wanted to find was a workable route around the north of Asia. When poor Le Maire and Schouten turned up in Batavia with what was regarded there as a fairy tale about finding open sea south of this new place Cape Horn, their logs were declared forgeries and they were flung in jail. On the way back to Holland to stand trial for his "lies," Le Maire died.

If the Dutch had only known it, the Englishman Francis Drake, in his little *Golden Hind*, had observed and reported on the open seas south of all America over thirty-five years before any Hollander tried to sail that way. Drake sailed through the Strait of Magellan and was driven south again by westerly gales on the Pacific side. As a prudent seaman, he let his ship drive freely to the south rather than see her forced by the high winds and seas upon the land. Before he had a chance to get to windward and to the north away from the dangerous land, he had noted the joining place down there of the Pacific and Atlantic seas.

Drake sailed from Plymouth, in England, in 1577, with orders to find and examine the mysterious continent of the South Seas known vaguely as Terra Australis and, after that, to sail through the Northwest Passage back to the Atlantic from the Pacific around the top of North America. This was another "route" which brave men had already lost their lives trying to find from the Atlantic side.

In fact, there was such a way, but, like that around the north of Asia, it had to wait until the days of power-driven icebreakers to be of any use, and icebreakers are expensive vessels. Neither the Northeast nor the Northwest passages, as these routes are called, is of any real commercial use, even now.

Drake found no Terra Australis, nor did anyone else, for that matter, where the sprawling southern continent was alleged to be. It took a great seaman some two centuries later to pin down that myth where it belonged. There was not one very large unknown southern continent. There were two small continents, Australia (more in the Indian Ocean than the Pacific) and the Antarctic, a useless land behind and under impenetrable ice, good for whales, penguins, and a few intrepid explorers.

As for Drake, his famous circumnavigation was a tremendous feat of sailing, no matter what he did not find or what he "pirated." Romping up the west coast of South America with the favoring north-going Humboldt Current, striking at defenseless Spanish ships and ports along the whole coastline (defenseless because they thought themselves impregnable; even ships with guns left them ashore to carry larger cargoes), Drake continued to Central and North America. He was in a bay very close to San Francisco and annexed the land now known as California for his Queen Elizabeth in the name of New Albion —an act which did not stick.

Then, with his ship full of treasure, he sailed across the North Pacific with the north equatorial current and the north-

National Maritime Museum, Greenwich, England
Sir Francis Drake

east trade winds. (When the average rate of progress of small ships on long voyages was about five knot, a two- or three-knot current was important.) Raiding the Spice Islands, making a "treaty" with their sultan for the promotion of English trade, getting on a reef and off again undamaged, the competent, whiskered little Englishman continued through the islands of Indonesia, across the Indian Ocean again with favoring currents and winds, around the Cape of Good Hope from east to west with yet another good current to assist him. Thence, the southeast trade blew him to the Equator. Working his way up the North Atlantic the way the Portuguese did, he was back in Plymouth by the end of September, 1580, after such a voyage as had never before been made. A ship of Magellan's and a handful of Magellan's men had made a successful circumnavigation, it is true, but Drake was the first leader who sailed his own ship right around the world.

One has descriptions of him, a confident little man sitting in his airy great cabin while his musicians played for him as he drank from golden goblets and ate from golden plates, both filched from Spain's ships and possessions, with the dark figure of a captured Portuguese pilot sitting dark-bearded and worried at his table. This was Nuno da Silva, whom Drake had taken out of his Portuguese ship as he ran south with the northeast trades past the Cape Verde Islands.

Drake had a huge chart which he had somehow acquired from the Lisbon cartographers. He had to rely on Portuguese and Spanish information, and he did not care how he obtained it. Poor Da Silva, carried from his Atlantic trader right through the Strait of Magellan and through the Pacific to Central America, was only one of his captured pilots. Another was Alonso Sanchez Colchero, described as a pilot for the China trade. The rank of pilot meant navigator then, not one who knows the way into only one port as it does today. The knowledge of such pilot-navigators was still their personal possession and chief qualification, earned the hard way by many years of observant and dangerous seafaring.

Pilot Colchero took no great liking to sea-roving Captain Drake. He would not help, nor did a spell shackled in irons make any difference to him. So Drake put a noose around his neck and swung him playfully a couple of times off the deck to give him a taste of his fate if he persisted in his obstinacy. The old man was still far from cooperative. As soon as he could, Drake changed him for yet another captured pilot who scared a little more easily.

Violins playing and bearded old pilots being swung off the deck, a hold stuffed with chests of stolen treasure and a maindeck with guns, the richest trimmings for the leader and six feet of wet maindeck for the crew to bed down in their cloaks— so the little *Golden Hind* wandered along on her wonderful voyage—right around the world, known and unknown, to the farthest south and farthest practical north (in the Pacific). Four times she sailed across the Equator, through *all* the zones of trade winds (in the Atlantic, twice), with almost *all* the favoring currents, making longer nonstop runs than ever had been made by anyone before—all this in a minute ship which today would not be allowed even to enter the yacht race to Bermuda (because she could not comply with the standards of seaworthiness laid down for that event) or, indeed, for the same reason, to clear from any civilized port in the world. . . . It was tremendous, fantastic. Above all it was the achievement of a great seaman with a brave crew. After that one voyage the English knew as much as any nation of the way of the sea and the routes across the ocean, and more than most.

Such knowledge spread rapidly when it could be turned to quick profit. Before long, others followed Drake, though none was ever again so successful. Many voyages added to this knowledge. French and English cut into Spanish trade in the West Indies islands. English ships were soon crossing the Atlantic as a trade route, not just raiding voyages. The circulatory movements of its currents and winds became known to them, too.

Colonists sailed across to Virginia long before the end of the sixteenth century. The first lot was taken off again at its own request, when the extraordinary Drake chanced to sail by in the Gulf Stream, bound homeward from some raiding excursion. The second lot, landed at Roanoke in the late 1580's, went missing and no trace of them has since been found. The third lot, a year or two later, again utterly disappeared—all ninety-one men, nine boys, and seventeen women. There was room enough in Virginia and all America beyond for over a hundred poor people to disappear, but it was odd that two whole parties should be lost so utterly.

The fourth lot stuck, to found Virginia at Jamestown in 1607: the fifth or sixth (for between times there had been an abortive attempt to settle the coast of Maine) in 1620 were the Pilgrim Fathers in their famous *Mayflower*.

As for the difficulties of sailing ships like those, and the hardships for passengers, I have had a little experience of my own from the westward delivery voyage of the replica *Mayflower* from Plymouth, Devon, to Plymouth, Massachusetts, in 1957. This new *Mayflower* was a small wooden ship just as the Elizabethans had been—small and high, with an oddly shaped hull and light wooden spars, supported by rope rigging.

By 1600 or so English merchant-ships were up to two hundred tons and light topsails had sprouted over their big lower sails. Otherwise they were the same as they had been for several hundred years—three-masters with a long, unsupported bowsprit, an awkward sail like an Arab's lateen (but not so well rigged) on the third mast, big sails called courses on the other two, those of the middle mast, called main, being much larger than those on the fore. There was also an extremely awkward and sometimes dangerous sail set on a spar across the bowsprit. This was the spritsail. The seamen had no aids to the heavy labor essential in their work, save a primitive capstan. The rigging was complicated and much beset by chafe. That is, many parts wore themselves thin or cut right through simply by rubbing on other parts, as the ship jumped and pitched and rolled in the sea.

All the rigging worked. It was not rigid. The masts rolled a couple of feet more than the ship did. Reefing was unknown, and sail area could be increased only by attaching extra pieces to the bottom of the principal sails. These extra pieces were called bonnets, and they could quickly be taken off again. The ships leaked. There was no accommodation except in the great cabin and a few miserable hutches set up temporarily in that part of the ship. Water was kept in stinking barrels and the food was appalling. Passengers and crew relieved themselves squatting on a piece of the ship built out on the hull, jutting out ahead and called the "heads." Here the sea broke whenever the wind was fresh, and there were the joint dangers of being blown off or drowned.

In heavy weather, when the wind blew violently, the only thing the ship could do was to shorten down drastically: as soon as it blew a gale, every sail must be secured and the topmasts lowered to reduce the weight aloft. In such a state the ship would lie quite safely (as we discovered with the new *Mayflower*). Very naturally, she would also drive furiously to leeward, for her high sides offered a great area for the gale to blow upon. This was discouraging but safe, provided there was plenty of sea room to leeward and no land in the way; if there were, it was too bad. How could a ship which was unable to set a stitch of sail claw back into the shrieking gale? She was a plaything in the sea. Anchors are no use in unsheltered waters.

When the sea is assaulting the ship and flinging her about, they will not hold.

I thought of Drake often, on that *Mayflower* voyage, and his *Golden Hind* driven among the dreadful seas that rise violently like vicious ship-killing monsters and rage down near Cape Horn. No wonder afterward he kept to azure seas, if he could.

As for navigation, real ability to fix a ship's position at sea, even with approximation, was impossible until the time of Cook. With no means of establishing longitude, all was guesswork. An early English directory for sailing the North Atlantic (a sort of sixteenth-century *Periplus*) could only advise master mariners when "on a bonne voyage, hoyce up the saile and let God steere"—advice which did not appeal even to the Pilgrim Fathers.

One of the outstanding characteristics of the new *Mayflower* was her infinite capacity for throwing herself about. In anything of a seaway one just had to hang on—hang on for life aloft, hang on for limb on deck—for she flung her mastheads round in circles, her rigging in thrashing bights, and her poop like a treetop growing from a precipice, in a hurricane.

In the meantime, the Dutch, doing very well with their bluff, big ships in the trade to the Indies, worked out or found out a new sailing route over the Indian Ocean. Until their time, ships worked from the Cape of Good Hope to India or Java by hugging the Cape and then using the trade winds, both coming and going. The Dutch soon observed the useful west wind drift of the so-called southern ocean current which, becoming the west Australian current south of Java, combined there with the trade wind to bring heavily laden ships to the north. Instead of sailing outward diagonally across the Indian Ocean, it was much better for a well-found ship to dip down to the south well before Good Hope and, taking the stormy west winds behind

her, run swiftly before them to the approximate longitude of
Java. Then, swinging up to the north, she could sail before the
trades.

The route was longer but the winds were better, and faster
passages could be made this way. One catch was in that word
"approximate," for ships still could not establish their longitude. Running blindly before a series of cyclonic gales, they
could underestimate, turn north too late, hit the somewhat solid
but then useless coast of southwest or west Australia. As the
years passed, many did. These coasts are still littered with their
bones and their names. But the Dutch seamen stuck to the new
route, and in due course others followed them.

The wind and current system of the Indian Ocean went
round and round just as those of the Atlantic and the North
Pacific did. Having gained it, sailors exploited this knowledge.
The last ocean of mystery for them was the South Pacific. After
the spasmodic use of the immensely long and difficult route via
the Strait of Magellan and after a very few brave spirits had
won a way past Cape Horn—a few Dutchmen and the English
admiral Anson on a circumnavigation—seamen concentrated
on the Good Hope route, and the Dutch set up a wayside stop
there at Cape Town early in the seventeenth century for the
refreshment of their fat-bellied, heavily laden ships.

These Dutchmen went at the Indian Ocean trade in a
thorough-going manner. If the Portuguese had pioneered it,
they were determined to profit from it to the maximum, and, if
possible, forever. Between 1595 and 1601 alone, sixty-five
Dutch ships in no fewer than twenty-two fleets sailed to the
East, only one of them even bothering to use the Strait of
Magellan. French and English East India companies tried to
cut in, but it was a long time before either prospered. Chartered in London in 1600, little over a decade since the defeat
of the Spanish armada, the English East India Company was

established both in India and the Persian Gulf thirty years later and had founded Bombay in 1665.

In time, it was this English company which did best. For centuries there was a working arrangement by which the English controlled most of the Indian trade, and the Dutch that of Indonesia. Both did well.

By this time the general sailing routes of the world were pretty well laid down. Da Gama on his first voyage discovered the Agulhas and Mozambique currents when he had to sail against them. Knowledge of the best routes across the Indian Ocean soon followed the fleets of Portuguese, Spanish, Dutch, English and French ships. The enterprising American, Benjamin Franklin, put the Atlantic's Gulf Stream on the charts in 1770, at a time when he was postmaster-general of the American colonies. Knowledge of its effects was important to the carriage of the mails. A strange Englishman named Dampier, who seems to have been at times a buccaneer, a privateer, and a pioneer in the study of elementary oceanography and was on the coast of northwestern Australia by 1688 (the place appalled him), produced a couple of books about ocean winds. These showed sound knowledge and were most useful.

Still the great Pacific south of the trade-wind zones remained unsailed. About the middle of the eighteenth century there was at last an interest in it. If there really were any Terra Australis in the neighborhood, it could hardly fail to offer profitable trade. Who was going to be first? The Dutch had a good idea that any continent in the temperate zone was no new Asia, or America, for their competent countryman Abel Janszoon Tasman had—without knowing it—already pinned down Australia where it must be. Tasman had circumnavigated the whole continent in 1642, out of sight of it and without knowing quite what he was doing. He had then discovered both Tasmania and New Zealand.

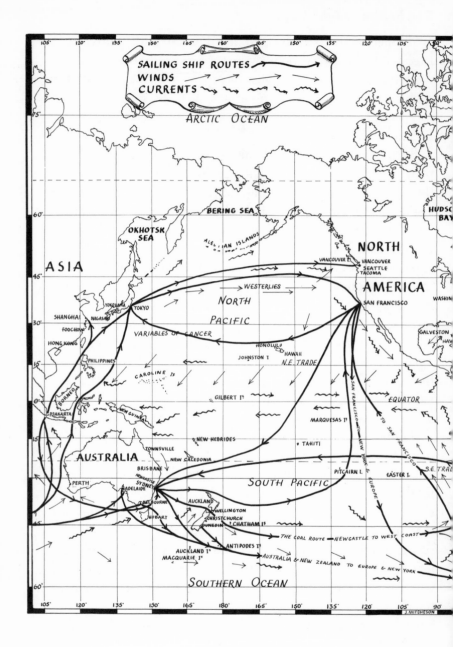

SAILING SHIP ROUTES
WINDS
CURRENTS

ARCTIC OCEAN

BERING SEA

OKHOTSK
SEA

ALEUTIAN ISLANDS

ASIA

NORTH

VANCOUVER I.   VANCOUVER
                SEATTLE
                TACOMA

AMERICA

SAN FRANCISCO

WASHIN

WESTERLIES

YOKOHAMA

NORTH

SHANGHAI   NAGASAKI   TOKYO
FOOCHOW

PACIFIC

VARIABLES OF CANCER

HONG KONG

GALVESTON
HAV

PHILIPPINES

HONOLULU
          HAWAII
JOHNSTON I.
          N.E. TRADE

CAROLINE IS

BORNEO

EQUATOR

DJAKARTA

NEW GUINEA

GILBERT IS

MARQUESAS IS

NEW HEBRIDES

TAHITI

SAN FRANCISCO TO NEW YORK & EUROPE

AUSTRALIA

TOWNSVILLE
          NEW CALEDONIA
BRISBANE

SOUTH PACIFIC

PITCAIRN I.

EASTER I.

PERTH

NEWCASTLE
SYDNEY
ADELAIDE

S.E. TRA

MELBOURNE   AUCKLAND
          WELLINGTON
HOBART   CHRISTCHURCH
          DUNEDIN   CHATHAM IS

TO SAN FRANCISCO

THE COAL ROUTE   NEWCASTLE TO WEST COAST

ANTIPODES IS

AUCKLAND IS
MACQUARIE IS

AUSTRALIA & NEW ZEALAND TO EUROPE & NEW YORK

SOUTHERN OCEAN

J. MITCHESON

126

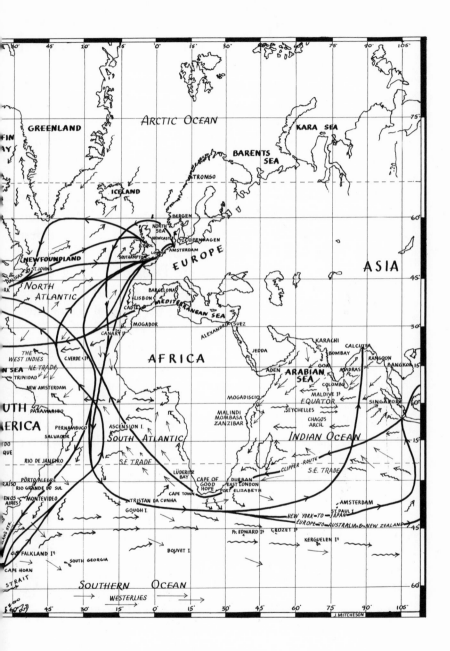

From the Dutch East India Company's viewpoint he and other Dutch seamen groping along Australia's north had established what was to them a more important fact, known a century earlier to the Portuguese. This Terra Australis place, whatever else it might be, was of no use to European trade. It was a dusty, fly-blown desert, inhabited by the most primitive people in the world; they were still in the Stone Age.

But England was interested, too. Their Commodore John Byron commanded a fine coppered frigate named the *Dolphin* on the first English probe into the South Seas, in 1764. Byron was known in the navy as "Foulweather Jack," and his eldest son was "Mad Jack," the poet Lord Byron's father. He made a fine, fast circumnavigation with the *Dolphin,* rushing across the Pacific and out of it again as rapidly as possible around the north of New Guinea, seeing nothing whatever of Terra Australis and precious little of anything else, except the sea.

After him came others who did no better but did it with not quite the same dash and speed. The one who tried to do better, Philip Carteret, was handicapped by a poor ship and a poorer commanding officer named Wallis who, after taking Carteret's stores, sailed away and left him to his own devices in his feeble, slow, and utterly preposterous vessel. Even at that, Carteret made a determined sweep of the South Pacific beyond the trade-winds area and sailed his awful ship until she all but fell to pieces and most of his crew were down with scurvy.

In the meantime, Wallis in the *Dolphin* was at luscious Tahiti, which had been discovered shortly before by the brilliant Frenchman Bougainville. From the pleasures of Tahiti, Wallis rushed along the beaten track to further refreshment at the island of Tinian, far off in the North Pacific. One after another, these men who could have achieved so much skipped across the Pacific as if they were afraid of the place and contrived one and all—except Bougainville—to keep far off the

The *Endeavour* in which James Cook criss-crossed the enormous area of the vast South Sea

Great Barrier Reef of Australia, almost as if they were aware of its threatening existence. Bougainville got among the outlying reefs and promptly—and prudently—hauled off again. At that time, though Torres had sailed through Torres Straits long before, the Barrier Reef and all the east coast of Australia were not on any available maps at all.

A quiet north-country seaman put an end to that. His name was Cook—James Cook, and his home port was Whitby in Yorkshire, England. His ship was no swift frigate but a converted Whitby collier renamed *Endeavour*. With her and other ships, over the following decade, he criss-crossed the enormous area of the vast South Sea as that sea was never sailed before or since. He circumnavigated Antarctica. He charted New Zealand, discovered and charted the east coast of Australia, discovered New Caledonia, much of the New Hebrides, the Cook and Friendly Islands; he sailed around Cape Horn both ways from east to west and west to east. He established the fact that in the South Pacific, too, the currents and the ocean winds went around and around in an anticlockwise direction, just as in the Indian and South Atlantic. He pioneered that last great sailing route—the wild run before the west winds in high latitudes from the Pacific to the Atlantic around Cape Horn.

Cook himself was hacked to pieces on a Hawaiian beach, toward the end of his third voyage. His work was done. There were a few illustrious seamen who accomplished something here and there after him—the Englishmen Flinders, Vancouver, Puget, Bligh; the Frenchmen D'Entrecasteaux, La Perouse, Freycinet, Marion-Dufresne (who was eaten by the Maoris at New Zealand's Bay of Islands).

Of them all James Cook was the first and by far the greatest. After his three tremendous voyages, even the vast Pacific could offer his successors only some atolls and reefs, and a few old islands.

Chapter 11 • THE STORY OF THE SHIP

THERE WAS A TREMENDOUS DIFFERENCE BETWEEN COMMO-
dore Byron's frigate *Dolphin* and Captain Cook's excollier *Endeavour,* but both were excellent ships. The *Dolphin* was a
fighting ship, her bulwarks and upper sides pierced with gunports through which, when opened, cannons thrust their noisy
snouts to belch iron balls as necessary. She could carry her
fighting needs and the requirements of her large crew, and that
was all. Her lean hull, with its fine underwater lines, could not
take the ground, as seamen say. That is, she had to be afloat,
properly supported in the sea, or she would fall over.

Any ship provided for him, said Cook, "must be of a construction that will bear to take the ground"—that is, stand upon
the shallow sea bed, not fall over and wreck itself on it—"and of
a size which, in case of necessity, may be safely and conveniently
laid on shore to repair any accidental damage. These properties
are not to be found in ships of war of forty guns, or frigates, or
in East India Company's ships, or in large three-decked West
India ships, or indeed in any other but north-country ships such
as are built for the coal trade."

How right he was proved to be when the *Endeavour,* sailing
for the first time inside the long labyrinth of the Great Barrier
Reef off the northeast coast of Australia, struck on a reef and
had to be grounded for repairs. Cook made her sound again,
heaved her off the beach, and sailed back to England. As a coal
carrier trading on the east coast of England, the *Endeavour* had

131

to be able to sit on the mud flats while her coal was unloaded. An awkward, almost clumsy little thing to look at—she was less than four hundred tons—she was a slow sailer but immensely safe, for her tubby hull shook off the assaults of the sea like a barrel and her decks were safe to work on even in the wildest storm. But they were horribly exposed. She must have been a very uncomfortable ship in far southern latitudes. She had a straight, unprotected upper deck and even what passed as her quarter-deck had no shelter at all. Her helmsman and her watchkeepers stood in the open and took what came. She was a ship for the toughest of the tough seafarers of those days, from her captain downward.

At that time, all these sea-going wooden ships were rigged in much the same way—English, Dutch, French, Spanish, Baltic, Portuguese. Hull forms might differ greatly but much the same sail plan drove the lot. There were huge cargo carriers such as the carracks of Portugal and the East Indiamen, big sea-wagons whose principal function was to sail to India somehow, gorge themselves with cargo there, and then somehow sail back again. If they took a year for one voyage it didn't matter, so long as they got home at all. They had to be able to fight when needs be. Most of them looked more like fighting ships than the passenger-cargo-liners which they were. Their bulwarks and 'tween-decks were pierced for guns and they carried big crews to fight. There is a record of one group of sixteen which, pretending to be ships-of-the-line, opened up on a French fleet and scared them off.

These East Indiamen were the Cunarders of their day except in the matter of speed (which didn't count); the West India-men were smaller, Atlantic copies. There were also tramps, ships not built for any special trade but able to bring timber and hemp and turpentine from the Baltic, wine in tuns from France and Spain, coals from Newcastle, wool to Flanders, dried and salt fish from Newfoundland, timber and tobacco from Virginia.

There were a surprising lot of these ships. Ships and trade made more trade and slowly improved living conditions for everyone.

Most of these ships were three-masters of the old school—full-rigged ships—built of wood as solidly as possible, with one mast well forward, another in the center of the ship (more or less), and a third mast somewhere aft. The two more important masts—always the fore and main—were made of three separate spars. The lower spar was always a very solid piece of tree, stepped—that is, standing firmly—on the keelson, on the inside of the bottom of the ship. It rose through the deck high enough to carry a yard from which a large square sail was set. Above this lower mast was another, secured by a rather cumbersome arrangement. This was called the topmast. As the centuries rolled by, a third and lighter piece of mast was fitted to the top of the topmast. This was the topgallant.

On each of these masts a square sail was set from a yard smaller than that on the lower mast. All these yards hoisted and lowered for the convenience of setting and taking in sail. The yards were swung by ropes and tackles called braces, to trim the sails for shifts of wind or alterations of course. The bowsprit still carried a spritsail, but now it spread triangular sails called jibs as well. These were set as they are aboard yachts today, by hauling the pointed head up toward a convenient place on the foremast.

Other such triangular sails took up the space between the masts. Behind the mizzen—always a much shorter mast than the main—was an improved lateen. This sail set entirely behind the mast, where it could be swung across easily. It was a very useful sail to maneuver the ship and help the steering.

A great tracery of rope-rigging of all shapes and sizes had

long been in use to support and control the masts and sails. This appeared most complicated to the landsmen of those times and still does today. Essentially, it was simple. Every rope was there for a definite purpose. It was placed one way, led one way, had its own name and its own spot on deck. A sailor could step from one ship to another and be perfectly at home within ten minutes. He "knew the ropes" on the blackest night as well as the fairest day. He could "hand, reef, and steer," which means that he could make all the necessary knots and splices in cordage, handle sail in the wildest gale on the highest yard and, with his shipmates, keep on fighting the sail until it was secured, and he could stand his "trick" at the wheel.

Both officers and seamen were extremely conservative. Their calling made them so. Any experiment with ships was also with their lives. Having once evolved an efficient ship which could survive at sea and make useful voyages, they were against change—*all* change, even for the better. They liked square sails

In the Atlantic trade winds—the Swedish school-ship C. B. *Pedersen*

Alan Villiers

because yards were more manageable than lateens. As ships increased in size, square sails increased with them, far beyond the
point of practicability for any other sort of sail. When they became too large, square or oblong sails could be divided into two
by halving the sail and setting the two halves on separate yards.
The lateen could never be subdivided like that.

As ships grew, masts were built up higher. Sails were set
higher and higher—royals, skysails, moonrakers. Square sails
could be extended in area in good sailing winds (like the
trades) by adding extension pieces to them called studding
sails. The size of the lateen could be increased only by lowering the yard and lashing an extra piece to the end of it, then
changing to a larger sail. This was very awkward, caused a great
deal of work and loss of way while it was being done and, more-
over, there was a definite limit to the size of the sail that could
be carried. So the rule was square sails for ocean voyaging, right
from medieval days until the end of the deepsea sailing era. A
sailing-ship sailor from a Cape Horner of the early 1950's (when
only two such ships were still sailing) could step back aboard
the old *Mayflower* and, within an hour, work out the complica-
tions of her Elizabethan rig, "hand, reef, and steer" aboard her
just as in his modern ship. (Some did, or I could never have
sailed that replica.) As for frigates, ships-of-the-line, East Indiamen and West Indiamen, any square-rigger man could take the
lot in his stride.

True, he might find conditions aboard somewhat irksome
were he really called upon to step back through the centuries.
Matters like food and accommodation and the general treatment
of seamen could be very annoying indeed, for the deepsea sailor
was regarded as expendable right until the twentieth century.
His food was appalling and his quarters what he might make
of some below-decks hutch in an insanitary, wet, and ill-venti-
lated (or else too well-ventilated) part of the stinking ship. He

Discipline was harsh, and flogging was the usual punishment in the old days.

might be flogged, ducked from the yardarm or keel-hauled, if he had bad officers. He could die of scurvy at sea or fever ashore, and no one would bother about him. His wages were a pittance. Worst of all, he could be press-ganged—seized and forcibly enlisted—into the navy in time of wars, real or impending, and as far as he was concerned the navy was even worse than the merchant service. At least an East Indiaman, if he survived a voyage, could draw his pay and leave on return to his home port. In the navy he was lucky if he had either pay or leave while war lasted.

In the old days, the seaman was far more subject to shipwreck and drowning. Overloaded East Indiamen foundered, got on rocks or lee shores, and broke to pieces, were sometimes seized by enemies or pirates. After every severe storm, the east coast of England was littered with the wrecks of poor little

North Sea traders driven up there, and the flaxen-haired bodies washed up on the beaches for weeks.

The way of the sea was hard.

It was almost as hard as the iron, then steel, that took the place of wood in ship construction both for hulls and then for masts and yards; for the size of big sailing ships doubled and trebled but crews were cut down. As the ships were stronger, they stayed longer at sea and made more difficult voyages, habitually fighting a way westward past Cape Horn on Chilean and Peruvian voyages and passages between Europe and the west coast of North America. Where the wooden ships had been slow and high and (unless they sank or hit the land) reasonably safe to work aboard, these steel ships were long and low and raced through the seas like half-tide rocks, spilling men overboard, throwing them from their bowsprits which dug too often right into the sea. They were laden heavily down, and they fought their way at sea from voyage-beginning to voyage-end. As a result they were wet and uncomfortable, and could be dangerous.

In the old days, the easy-going East Indiamen reduced sail at night and took no risks (except of getting ashore, perhaps). If the principal reason for this was to allow the old captain (and his important passengers) a good night's sleep, the seamen benefited also, for there were plenty of them to cope with the extra work of reducing sail at night and setting it again next morning.

This sloppy way of sailing came to an end before the days of iron ships. Easy-going voyaging was based on monopoly. In England, for example, there was only the one East India Company; so long as its cargoes reached the market at all they were immensely profitable. The company controlled that trade more or less as it liked. There were fortunes for all. A captain could retire with a fortune after three voyages, if he looked after things properly. Owners did even better. The riches of the East still came by what amounted to parcel trade. They were for the rich who could afford high prices. The change from a high-priced parcel trade and a rigidly controlled, profiteering monopoly to cheap bulk and free trade was a shock which owners, masters, and seamen alike put off as long as possible. Seafaring nations fought wars to maintain things as they were.

All this was knocked on the head forever by the clipper ship from the new United States of America which not only cut in on established trades and upset monopolies but began positively to hustle ships as they had never been hurried before. The Americans drove their lean, lithe, and heavily sparred tall ships *day and night* from voyage-beginning to voyage-end.

This was new: it had to be met. What the Americans could do the Scots and English must do likewise, if not better. This was the era of the wonderful clipper races when, instead of shortening down their slow-moving charges, gorging themselves with their rich passengers on a splendid nine-course dinner and varied wines before turning in for a good night's sleep, masters —lean and lithe and tall like their ships—catnapped in deck chairs on their reeling poops while they drove their magnificent ships to get every last knot out of them, to make them shift nonstop over the colossal distance between the tea ports of China and the auction marts of London faster than man had ever moved anything across the seas before.

Drive and race, and let the gale howl in the strong rigging! Drive and keep on driving! Shortcut through the islands of the China and the Java seas, dodge among the reefs (maybe hit one sometimes; that was too bad), cut down the miles, step up the speed, and the devil take the hindmost.

The London market loved this. A big bonus awaited the first master to land new season's teas. This was the wonderful era when ships like the *Ariel* and the *Taeping*, sailing from their

The Great Tea Race of 1886 between the *Ariel* and the *Taeping*, as painted by Gordon Grant

China port together, raced sixteen thousand miles never seeing one another again until both came storming up the English Channel at the end like the magnificent ocean yachts they were. On they raced, streaking past the steamships as they raced neck and neck, pyramids of white sails leaning gracefully upon the sea as the glorious hulls, spray-covered, spume to the mastheads, tore up-channel in the grandest sailing spectacle ever seen by man. The steamships' men turned to cheer them as they were overhauled. Crowds gathered on the Channel cliffs and beaches to admire the sight as these glorious, impeccable thoroughbreds came racing by.

For all felt that these were the quintessence of sailing-ship evolution. These were wonderful and heart-stirring ships. They were the ultimate development, at least of fast sailing-ships in the China trade.

There were other clippers—plenty of them. They raced out to California in the Gold Rush and again to Australia when gold was discovered there, powerful big two-thousand-tonners like the wonderful *James Baines, Lightning, Champion of the Seas*—ships which claimed runs of four hundred miles and more a day, and cut the sailing time to Australia from five or six months to two.

But it was all in vain.

While the graceful *Taeping* and *Ariel* stormed westward past Good Hope, ten thousand lean, dark hands were tearing at the Egyptian sand five thousand miles away, digging a canal through the narrow neck of land joining Africa to Asia—this time a canal for ocean-going ships, which would not silt up and be forgotten. The year was 1866. Three years afterward the modern Suez Canal was opened. This was doom to the clipper ships. No matter how beautifully they were designed or how strongly rigged and bravely sailed, they could not hope to stand up to competition through this shortcut they could not use.

It was no use to them. Going through the canal would not benefit them. For the way of sail on the oceans could never be through that ditch. It was strictly for steamships.

There were deep-sea cargo-carrying sailing ships for ninety years after that; but they were big steel cargo-carriers, bulk-movers of coal, grain, lumber, nitrates, guano. For another fifty years after Suez they fought the steamships; for thirty years there were owners to back them who thought they still might win. As late as the first decade of the twentieth century, big engineless sailing ships were still being built in Scotland and Germany. German, French, British, American, and Scandinavian sailors did their best to carry on in world trades.

The Americans concentrated for years on the fore-and-aft rig, developing large schooners for their own coastwise and transpacific trades. Three-, four-, and five-masters became six-masters

—even one seven. The schooners were economical and useful vessels. There were trades such as soft coal from Virginian ports which they suited, and in these they managed to make a living for many years after steamships should have ousted them. In the end, the big schooners were put out of business by towed barges and trucks.

These schooners could be sailed with a working crew of one man a mast, plus a large steam donkey engine to lighten the heavy jobs of hoisting the sails, getting the anchor up, and so on. In the Pacific, the trade winds suited them almost ideally for the run to Australia. But when it came to real world-circling sailing, they were greatly inferior to the square-rig despite the fact that, size for size, square-riggers required three times the crew.

The one seven-masted schooner built was so big and clumsy she could scarcely get out of her own way. She made few voyages and drove up on the coast of the Scilly Islands the first time she tried to cross the North Atlantic.

Square-rigged ships were very useful bulk-carriers in certain trades, particularly coal from Newcastle, New South Wales, across the South Pacific with the strong westerly winds of the Roaring Forties (the sailors' name for those areas where the wind was frequently roaring) and then back again with nitrates from Chile or guano from Peru, before the southeast trade winds. Many big ships sailed from Australia to Chilean ports in better than tramp-steamer time.

But that was in vain, too. The trade left them, principally because of the unfortunate perversity of the miners in New South Wales, who went on strike so often that even their best customers had to look for their coal elsewhere. Then some scientist discovered how to extract nitrate from the air, and Chilean nitrates suffered.

The last of the big sailing ships survived in two last trades—between Germany and the west coast of South America, and from South Australian outports to northwest Europe with grain. Some of these German ships were as outstanding in their way as the best of the clippers ever were. The Germans had the most powerful, the strongest, and the most consistently well-sailed big sailing ships that ever were. The Hamburg five-masted full-rigged ship *Preussen* of 1902—the only such ship built—averaged better than 7 knots throughout her entire sea-going life and could do 17½ in a gale. Unlike the clippers with their parcel cargoes, she carried eight thousand tons. Unlike them, too, she had a comparatively small crew—forty-two all told. Many a thousand-ton clipper had that many able seamen.

The *Preussen* was so fast that in the end her own speed killed her. A cross-Channel steamer, unable to believe that she was doing better than 12 knots, tried to cut across her bows one day off Dover in 1910. Too late she realized her error: she smashed into the *Preussen* and knocked her headgear and her foremast down. Handicapped in this way the five-master drove ashore; a gale came up and finished her.

What was it like to command such ships? We are the last generation to know. There was a great exhilaration, a superb sense of satisfaction and achievement in handling one of these engineless Cape Horn ships on a voyage, say, from South Australia nonstop to the United Kingdom. I have been in a big sailing ship which did it in eighty-three days—sixteen thousand miles at an average speed of 8 knots carrying fifty-six hundred tons of bagged wheat, with a crew of four men and twenty boys. I have done it in my own small full-rigged ship from Tahiti, as part of a voyage around the world.

Day after day the ship, alone in the wild immensity of the endless sea, rushes on before the gale. The wind screams, the

Alan Villiers

The last square-rigger on the Banks, the barkentine *Gazela* of Lisbon

sea rises. Will it continue to rise and overwhelm the ship? For all such ships are vulnerable if imperfectly sailed. I can name twenty stout steel four-masters and ships missing down there. I know the beautiful clipper *Ariel* sailed under in the end. I know there is ice. I know that despite a good chronometer checked by radio-time signals, a rotating modern log, a perfect sextant, and the best of government-sponsored nautical tables, navigation can still go wrong.

I know my limitations. I walk the reeling poop, I cling beneath the weather cloth lashed in mizzen or jigger-rigging, as stinging hail lashes out of the night. Before the bow rushes a roll of foam so wide and white that it throws up light—the only light we have, for the ship sails blacked-out save for the binnacle's fitful and uncertain gleam. At the wheel two lads strain to keep the ship running truly upon her course—within a compass point each side, at best—while the seas rage, lifting high astern as if intent upon one thing only, to fall upon and utterly destroy my running ship, to sweep her end for end, flood her from bulwark to bulwark, drive her down in her headlong way.

Shall I heave-to, stop? Will this great wind rise to such strength that I cannot sail before it, or, shifting quickly, so twist the sea that instead of running in long parallel crests it will become a snarling, tossed-up maelstrom in which no running ship can live? Heave-to! Heave-to! The coward in me shouts: heave-to while you have the chance!

For the hove-to ship will lie in safety, shoulder-to-the-sea like an albatross asleep, yielding, no longer fighting for her head and speed, no longer in danger of being overwhelmed. There is sea room. I can drift for days, and the drift will be in the right direction.

The masts roll, toss, lurch like forest giants in the torment of a hurricane. Somewhere high aloft I can hear the cries of the boy crew as they fight to save the remnants of a blown-out sail and, even against the agonizing tumult of the screaming wind, I can hear the frightful thunderous cannonade of blown-out canvas, hear the murderous and demoniacal shriek of torn strong wire lashing in the wind.

The ship runs on, flinging her masts now as if she seeks deliberately to toss them out, and with them, to hurl those boys into the sea. It is horrible how much more loudly the wind screams and the sea rises, when one has command.

Heave-to!

Yet I know the wind *should* ease. I have already hove-to three times in the weeks of that wild run. To heave-to I lose time, prolong the danger, give in, if only for the moment—or all night.

At the wind's slightest easing I will pay off again and let the ship drive before the wind. She is well snugged down. She still steers and handles well. No fatal weight of water yet breaks over her. . . .

Whatever decision is made is mine and mine alone. All lives aboard are in my hands.

I have three ribs broken by being flung across the poop earlier that day. I have catnapped twenty minutes in the past three gale-filled days.

But the ribs are lashed up tightly. Down there, sleep is for the dead.

I look to windward—no hope there! No sign of any easing! The storm howls, screams, roars, bellows with ear-jamming might as if it never could make any other sound and all silence has departed from the world forever. I look aloft. The boys are winning—no serious damage. A blown-out sail can be replaced in the morning. I look along the deck. The long bowsprit rearing high above some great comber of a sea that passes beneath the vessel with a hiss and snarl and lash of gale-blown spume points the way ahead, a single storm jib out there straining like a black iron triangle.

A sudden break—I see a star! A star to wind'ard—heave-to be damned! Drive on, drive on! Let her go!

We shall have five thousand miles more of this, and worse, perhaps, but to all of us it is the most satisfying and challenging, most adventurous and red-blooded calling in all the world. We envy no landlubbers with their soft dry beds. We envy no one.

Not a man or boy aboard would change that calling then for a million dollars. One feels that one can keep the ship's head up, fighting, only with one's mind and alert eyes.

Let her go! I'm glad I'm here!

Chapter 12 • **POWER**

STEAM WON, OF COURSE. THE ASTONISHING THING WAS THAT it took so long to drive the sailing ship from the seas. Steam engines pumped out mines in Cornwall and did other jobs ashore half a century before a small steam-driven towboat was pulling a few barges gingerly along the Forth and Clyde canals in Scotland, toward the end of the eighteenth century. Early steamships of odd and curious appearance were seen on the Delaware, the Clyde, and in the waters of New York, before Robert Fulton had his *Clermont* going successfully between Manhattan and Albany on the Hudson River in 1807.

Being successful on the quiet waters of a river, unfortunately her contemporaries decided that the river was the best place for power-driven ships. By 1819, the United States had the auxiliary ship *Savannah* crossing the Atlantic with the help of a pair of steam-driven paddles, and this was the first such ocean-going use of power. The *Savannah* was fitted with paddles that were rigged down and stowed on deck when not in use—which was most of the voyage. She used her small engine for eighty hours on her 29½-day run from New York to Liverpool. This was enough to get her intercepted as a ship afire and in urgent need of assistance off the coast of Ireland. The little ship—she was about three hundred tons—went back to America under sail and was wrecked not long afterward.

It was not until another twenty years had passed before anything like a real Atlantic "ferry" service was established. Many farsighted Americans appreciated the advantages to be gained by harnessing steam for ship propulsion, but the excellence of their sailing "packet" service on the Atlantic held back the evolution of the ocean-going steamship. There were good reasons. Early boilers ate through fuel like hungry giants. American ships burned wood, not coal (it was not until the 1850's that the United States was producing coal really suitable for boiler fuel). Boilers did much better on fresh water than salt, but the early steamers could not carry fresh water and coal as well. Even thirty years after the *Savannah's* crossing, steamships still had to spend one day in every four at sea with their engines stopped and fires out while the salt was cleaned from the boilers, and more sea water was then run in.

Rivers provided both boiler water and boiler fuel, for trees could be cut down on their banks.

So the United States set about developing those enormous, ornate, and sometimes dangerous sternwheelers which remained such a thrilling feature of the Mississippi and other great rivers for the following century. River steamers could be built up on wide, flat, bargelike hulls. They could carry enormous cargoes which, since they had merely to be pushed, shoved, or pummeled aboard and did not have to be stowed against sea motion, could be handled with extreme speed and efficiency.

"Steamboat 'round the bend!" passed into American folklore. The exciting scene of a couple of the huge white and gilded vessels, flames belching from their twin high funnels, sternwheels thrashing the brown river water as they raced along, became commonplace. Sometimes their boilers blew up. Hundreds of river travelers were scalded to death or drowned. But sternwheelers were popular and they were thrilling; they filled a real need.

The fear of early boilers bursting held back steamship development for years. Presented at last with a practical means of

The *Savannah*, first ship to use steam in the North Atlantic

driving ships for the first time since the invention of the oar, the great majority of owners and seamen would have none of it. Seamen hated the dirty, smelly smoke which begrimed their rigging. They were used to clean seafaring, and the early steamship was anything but that. They hated, too, the interference with their traditional open deck, so necessary to work a ship with sails—and steamships carried sail for at least half a century. Owners hated the wasteful loss of the best space in their ships, taken up by boilers, engines, fresh water, and fuel. Fuel earned no freight and shut out cargo.

To carry coal enough to keep their boilers going on a transatlantic run, early steamers had to leave port grossly overloaded. They were driven by paddles, not screw-propellers; when they were too deeply immersed the paddles would not work efficiently. Paddles were meant to beat the surface, not shove themselves through a mass of water. They also rolled out as the ship rolled. With one paddle too deeply immersed and the other right out of the water, ships were hard to steer. They waddled along, first this way then that. Yet it was a long time before an efficient propeller was evolved. The pessimists were against that, too.

It was the late 1830's before it seemed possible that steam could be established successfully on the Atlantic at all. Americans had then at least half of their wonderful continent still to exploit, and this took up most of their attention. "Go West, young man!" was advice which turned few American eyes toward the sea.

Across the Atlantic in the United Kingdom, enterprising businessmen found ideal conditions for exploiting the steam age. Unlimited coal and abundant iron ore, the peculiar genius of the lowland Scot and the northcountryman for the marine engine, useful and sheltered ports with vast pools of labor ready at hand to set up shipbuilding yards by the dozen or the hundred as required, a tradition of seafaring and—even more important—of ship-owning and ship management in world carrying trades, gave Britain great advantages.

A Nova Scotian named Samuel Cunard was the first man who really took a clear view of these matters. He came to Britain especially to establish a transatlantic steamship company; to run a line of ships, not just one handicapped freak trying to fight prejudice and establish the new idea by herself. This had been tried before, and brilliantly; but it did not catch on. Running steamships was obviously going to be a mighty expensive business, for years to come. The North Atlantic was a bad ocean, particularly for westbound shipping; it was no use for westbound steamships to take the easy way down in the trade winds. Sailing packets had scorned that route for many years, for it added too many miles.

Three things, Mr. Cunard saw, were essential to give steamships a chance. First was a minimum of four ships preferably identical; second, some form of assured income, as substantial as possible; and third—if it could be arranged—a monopoly. So expensive were the inefficient steamships of the day that he calculated that his line would have to earn a quarter of its entire capital outlay each year, just to stay in business. This was a tall order.

But there was guaranteed income to be earned for carrying the British mails. As the United States grew and prospered, more and more people were traveling, and the market for transatlantic passengers, Mr. Cunard foresaw, would increase rapidly if it were properly catered to. There were plenty of businessmen on both sides of the Atlantic who would soon appreciate the benefits of assured arrival of their cargoes, on regular dates known in advance and kept.

Mr. Cunard found backers and took the plunge. Four sistership were built, each of 1150 tons and 207 feet long, able to steam through the water at 9 knots. They were wooden paddlers with accommodation for 115 passengers and hold space for 225 tons of cargo. The passengers were housed in a large deckhouse on the afterdeck—not very well, according to Charles Dickens. The novelist traveled to America in 1842 by one of these early Cunarders. To him the deckhouse was like a big hearse, and his cabin reminded him of a coffin.

In some ways, the early liners were worse than sailing ships, which at least were usually steadied by their own sails. The general arrangement of things on deck continued much the same, as it had to do when steamships were really just sailing ships with the addition of noisy and cumbersome engines. The Cunarders were never auxiliary sailing ships. They were powered vessels which retained sail enough to control the ship should their engines break down.

From the beginning they prospered. For the first time, man could push his ships across on favored ocean voyages without the overriding consideration of winds and sea. From wood to iron, then to steel, from the paddle to the screw-propeller, from eleven hundred tons to eleven thousand, twenty thousand, thirty thousand, and finally to eighty thousand the great ships grew—never just with one new ship but always four sisters, or three, or, in the end, a pair such as the splendid *Queens,* properly to carry on a coordinated service on a firm schedule.

The ships were always run with scrupulous attention to detail, above all to safety. The Cunard Line began the system of running liners on defined liner lanes, westbound one way and eastbound another, to minimize collision danger in that often stormy and sometimes fogbound sea. It was Cunard which first introduced the system of burning white and colored steaming lights so that other ships would know what course a Cunard vessel was making and so gauge collision dangers and avoid them. Cunard instructions to masters and crews were explicit and detailed.

> Avoid familiarity with any particular set or portion of your passengers. Avoid national observations yourself and discourage them in others. . . . Be civil and kind to all passengers —they will value your services on deck looking after their interests safely more than talking with them in the saloons. . . .
>
> On making the land, never omit to verify your position by soundings. Rather lose time in heaving-to than run the risk of losing the vessel. . . .
>
> You will bear in mind that we are now impressing upon you strong rules, long laid down by us for the guidance of our captains, the terms of which are plain and unmistakable . . .

And so on.

The SS *United States*

Cunard did not have things all its own way, by any means. The United States Collins Line was building faster and better ships within ten years of Cunard's first mail contract. Congress gave Collins an enormous subsidy but took it away again. Collins had four ships but two were lost, one by collision and another missing with everyone aboard. Loss of its subsidy and the two ships put it out of business. French, German, American, Dutch, and Italian companies gave Cunard hot competition and some still do so. Several British companies have been worthy sharers of the Atlantic passenger trade. Since its beginning, 185 shipping companies have shared in this trade. In the 1960's there are still twenty-five regulars in the business, flying fifteen different national flags.

Since 1952, easily the fastest ship in the North Atlantic has been the $70 million superliner *United States* which has held the Blue Riband since July of that year. Built in a drydock at Newport News, Virginia, to a United States naval specification as a troopship-liner for use in time of war, the *United States* is owned and run by United States Lines. The completely fire-proof fifty-four-thousand-ton liner has cut down the time between New York and Europe to less than three and a half days. In 1952, she crossed from the Ambrose lightship off New York to Bishop Rock, off the entrance to the English Channel, in three days ten hours forty minutes, at an average speed of 35.6 knots. It is believed that she could better even this, if seriously called upon to do so.

The North Atlantic is a tremendous trade, and continues to flourish. From 1840 when Cunard began, to the end of the century, 20 million emigrants came by sea from Europe while America's population increased from some 17 to nearly 76 million and her foreign trade increased, roughly, ten times. There was plenty of work for steamships to the United States and to Canada as well.

And not just in the North Atlantic. Slowly the powered ship spread all around the world. That great *leviathan*, fifty years ahead of her time, the thirty-two-thousand-ton *Great Eastern*, was designed by the brilliant engineer Isambard Kingdom Brunel not for the Atlantic but for trade to the Indian Ocean. The idea behind the enormous ship was that she would be able, by herself, to monopolize, or at least centralize, a great deal of the Indian trade. Lesser ships would feed her with cargoes for transshipment in her tremendous holds.

The *Great Eastern* was regarded by her contemporaries as either a monstrosity or a joke, or both. Whatever any other ship had ever had she had more of—five funnels, six masts, the biggest paddlewheels afloat, and the largest propeller (twenty-four feet diameter, thirty-seven feet pitch), two enginerooms, bunker space for twelve thousand tons of coal, space to carry ten thousand troops or four thousand passengers and holds for six thousand tons of dry cargo besides, more cows in large, comfortably

The *Great Eastern*

padded stalls to provide more fresh milk for more passengers than had ever before been catered to (Cunard could keep only cows enough to provide for women and children). Once it took twenty-three men to steer her—the world record for helmsmen aboard any ship at one time. How they all got at the spokes of her great hand-steering wheels is not now known.

She also had more—far more—than her share of bad luck. It took three months to get her into the water. When she was at last afloat, there was no trade that wanted her. She broke Brunel's heart and he died before she got to sea. She lost both paddlewheels and her rudder in a gale (which also tossed a cow through the saloon skylight). Fitted for two thousand she never had more than two hundred first-class passengers, and her only success was achieved first as a cable layer and then as an outsized sideshow on the River Mersey, near Liverpool, where she ended her days.

The *Great Eastern* was before her time. Her hull was far ahead of the power available to drive it. She was an expensive failure, but a brave rather than a foolish one, except for her unfortunate shareholders. The remarkable thing is that she was built at all.

The opening of the Suez Canal gave cargo-carrying steamships and long-distance, slower liners their big chance, for it presented both with a safe route to the East and Australia with convenient wayside bunkering stops. As ships, boilers and engines improved, power gained inexorably. Perfection of the diesel internal-combustion engine helped.

As ships grew, so did the cargoes for them. If tea was so successful a beverage for the rich, then it was good business to grow the stuff in bulk elsewhere—in South India, Assam, Ceylon—and ship it back to wholesalers from there for maximum distribution. Fruit, meat, coffee, spices, grain for flour to make bread, cotton and wool to make clothes, timber and steel for building filled the capacious holds of good ships endlessly and always (except in slumps) there was demand for more.

The opening of the Panama Canal in 1916 further helped the powered vessel. So did the submarine telegraph and radio, the turbine engine, the oil-fired boiler and—in ports—stronger tugs, bigger lighters, and great batteries of fast-working dockside cranes. Powered ships cost a lot: they have to be kept moving.

The steamship and her sister the motorship, before long—except for a small and decreasing number of junks, dhows, and proas in Eastern seas—were doing all the sea carriage in the world. What once had been the luxuries of the rich they made available, in time, to everyman. What began as new luxuries, such as gasoline to drive motorcars and oil for home boilers, they stepped up rapidly to a billion-tons' business. Of all the thousands of ocean-going ships at sea today, one out of every three is a bulk oil-carrier, a tanker, keeping a worldwide schedule on whose successful maintenance a great proportion of the world's industry and transport now depends.

Some of these tankers, giants of anything from eighty thousand to a hundred thousand tons, would make Brunel's *Great Eastern* look like an unwieldy modern car ferry. Some of these

Aboard the nuclear ship *Savannah* on her first trip

same ferries could fit two of the first *Savannahs* on their decks.

Meanwhile, in March 1962, a new *Savannah*, more revolutionary in her day even than the old, made her sea trials from Yorktown, Virginia. This new *Savannah* is the first nuclear-powered ocean-going merchant ship in the world, a product of American ingenuity, know-how, courage and enterprise—the greatest advance in ship propulsion for a century. The clean-lined white ship—twenty thousand tons, twenty knots, seventy passengers, twelve thousand tons of cargo—can carry passengers and cargo for years and years without ever once refueling. She is essentially a turbine steamer. The nuclear plant supplies the steam; but it can go on doing that with high efficiency for years.

From the smoking little auxiliary *Savannah* of 1819, staggering once across the Atlantic, to the nuclear ship *Savannah*, able to make a dozen round-world voyages at 20 knots on a few pounds of fuel; from rickety little wooden ships to the 35-knot *United States,* the wonderful *France* and the Cunard *Queens!* In the short space of little more than a century, man's fight with and conquest of the ocean sea, by means of powered vessels, has been spectacular indeed.

Chapter 13 • **FISH AND FISHING**

HAVING LEARNED TO SAIL ON THE SEA (AND TO FIGHT ON IT when necessary) man had another aim—to kill everything in it he could get at. Fish, seals, whales—sometimes even birds—were his quarry, and still are. Fish was the earliest food of the coastal dwellers. For thousands of years, man has taken all the fish he could find, by ever-improving methods. By fine-mesh nets dragged along the bottom, or thrown around schools of fish, or drifted along just below the surface to catch fish by their gills; by lines with anything from one hook to a thousand; by traps along the beach or set down in the sea offshore, by circular nets flung by one man, as in so much of Asian waters, he has taken fish from the continental shelf of the coastal seas by the million, million tons.

Species such as the herring, mackerel, cod, haddock, sardine, salmon, tuna, and flatfish he has especially gone after, never with the slightest mercy, and, even today, with very little or no understanding of the problems that his overfishing must create. He learned to fish with a horrible efficiency before he took much interest in the fish themselves. They were there and he could catch them.

The poor fish lent itself admirably to primitive processes of preservation. It could be smoked, sun-dried, salted, pickled in barrels. It was easy to broil, bake, boil, fry. Many shellfish may be eaten raw and some fish, too. Seals gave furs and skins for clothing, sometimes for canoes and boats. Whales gave meat, blubber, oil. Sea birds are food, too. Some unfortunate species, like sub-Antarctic penguins at Macquarie Island, south of Tasmania, have even been boiled for their oil.* Another Tasmanian seafood bird is called the mutton bird, because it is supposed to taste like sheep.

Yet fish are also God's creatures and their ways are remarkable and frequently mysterious. Consider the eel, for example, which is found in abundance in the rivers, ditches, and often pools of western Europe and eastern America. How does it get there? For years no one had the least idea. No one ever saw eel larvae, or a ripe female eel; the eels came as "elver" and they came by the billions. It turned out that adult eels all swim to a remote spot in the Sargasso Sea—a warm and weed-littered backwash of the Gulf Stream drift, on the western side of the North Atlantic. To here, for reasons known only to themselves, adult European eels swam westward and the American adult eels swam eastward. Both spawned in the Sargasso Sea, mostly in just one particular part of it about halfway between the Leeward Islands and Bermuda.

Scientists have discovered by painstaking observation that the eggs are spawned some five hundred fathoms below the surface in this area. The European eels spend the first three years of their lives there slowly growing from minute fellows shaped like leaves into the elver form. The American "elver" reaches that form in one year only. There is good food for them in the Sargasso Sea. At three years of age the little Europeans leave the warm sea water and swim east in the Gulf Stream drift for the fresh-water streams and rivers of Europe; their American cousins have already headed west at the age of one year. They both originate in the same area. How is it that the two forms never fail to separate from each other and swim off each in its

---

* Remains of the plant for treating them were still at Macquarie Island in 1923.

own direction? All the adult eels die there; they cannot lead their young.

Scientists know that fish are very susceptible to temperature, pressure, salinity, and other features of sea water. But how? Do they each contain little built-in laboratories, or something of the kind? How do they navigate, as these "elvers" do and the salmon does?

I remember once visiting the tunafish traps off the coast of the Algarve in southern Portugal. Here each year, on or about a certain day in May, schools of fat tunafish come swimming in mysteriously from nobody-knows-where, bound for the Mediterranean somewhere to spawn. They come so regularly that an enormous system of nets is put down to receive them each year, and local tuna canning factories depend upon their annual migration. Some six miles of net are moored in the form of a large letter *L*, with a sort of corral at its point. The tuna once sighting the net or its shadow make for the corral. Here the bottom is raised and up they come with it. Once on the surface they are gaffed, hauled, and pitchforked into waiting boats—sometimes five or six hundred tuna at a time.

One of the most remarkable features of all this, I saw, is that the tuna appear to be led by flying fish, although normally they eat such fish. First to break surface when the tuna are trapped in the corral is always a group of flying fish, frequently fish of unusual size. There is nothing in the stomachs of the tuna. Why are the flying fish there? If they are, in fact, co-operating—doing the navigating—*how do they know where to go*, or why do they bother with the job at all? They can scarcely all be there by chance.

How odd it is that little plaice and little sole should still start life with two normal eyes, one each side of the head, as other fish; yet they need both eyes on the uppermost side when they lie flat on the bottom of the sea. Through some mysterious process, after the baby plaice has settled on the sea floor—always on its left side—the left eye begins to travel around its head to the right. This starts about the thirtieth day. By the forty-fifth day it has finished its extraordinary journey to the top of the head, and there it stays for life.

Why, for that matter, should the little plaice always settle on the sea bed on its left side? And the turbot always on its right? Or the succulent sole turn itself into a night prowler, groping its way along the sea bed, using tufts of sensory whiskers protruding from the blind side of its flat head? For what mysterious reason or purpose do the humble herring combine in billions in that extraordinary upsurge over hundreds of square miles of sea which European fishermen call the "swim"? Nobody has any real knowledge. For that matter, little is known of the life history of the herring at all, though it is—in its own waters—one of the most common fish.

All that is known of this herring "swim" is that suddenly—sometimes at sunrise, sometimes sunset—all the herring in the

On the Grand Banks—the doryman's business is a dangerous one.

Alan Villiers

keep themselves on the seaward sides of the currents they live in, and their different tacks were because of the clockwise an anticlockwise current circulations in the different hemispheres No one would suspect a jellyfish of having much intelligence yet it is a fact that, by this strange ability, they greatly reduced the chances of being blown out of their currents and swept ashore.

We used sometimes to see odd things from those sailing ships. Without any engine noise or thudding propeller to scare fish away, they were ideal for observation. From high aloft on the yards, working in the sunlight, I have seen giant sunfish glinting huge and globular a few fathoms down, like three-ton fishy soccer balls fitted with a head, tail, and slowly waving fins. I have seen flying fish with a wingspan of over two feet (by the look of them), but I have never seen a flying fish fly. They glide with diaphanous wings, spread like a sail-plane's. They can glide a hundred yards. Often they will give themselves a further stretch in the air by assisted take-off from a powerful, sculling flick of their tails on the crest of a passing sea, when they are almost at the end of their glide.

Flying fish could take gliding lessons from that most wonderful of all the bird gliders, the albatross. Yet I have seen the albatross stall and all but crash in the turbulent air to leeward of a big square-rigger's sails, rushing along toward Cape Horn. On such occasions the big bird gives an angry and disgusted look as he sweeps astern beside the poop. What are you asses up to? it seems to ask. Sailors in calms used to catch a few albatross by means of a metal triangle baited with a bit of salt pork. The albatross puts its beak in the triangle and won't let go. Pulled aboard, the ship's name or a brief message might be painted on a leg. In that way friends in other ships astern of us, if they caught the same albatross (as they sometimes did), would at least know that our ship was still afloat.

world seem to be surfacing with a mad and inexpli
citement at the same moment, filling the sea like
silvered lake so solid with their bodies one feels that c
ski upon them, or walk on snowshoes for miles and mi

At such times, drift-net fishermen from the nei
ports of Yarmouth and Lowestoft on the North Sea
England have landed 75 million herring in one night a
scarcely made a dint in the tremendous "swim." Some
there is no "swim" at all.

When I was a sailor in Scandinavian sailing ships
up from south Australia around the Horn into the
we used to see thousands of strange, small jellyfish flo
the warm currents. The sailors distinguished two types,
guese men-of-war" and what they called "by-the-winds
was a floating jellyfish about the size and shape of
conch shell. Each trailed long, stinging tentacles, whic
be up to forty feet long or more, and could give you
nasty sting if you touched one while swimming over t
in a calm. The man-of-war had a crinkly raised erection
the top of its body which acted as a sail. The by-the-wind
flatter sort of sail. Both seemed to spend their lives just
along, poisoning anything which touched their tentacles.

But we noticed a very extraordinary feature about then
In the southern hemisphere they sailed always on the por
and, in the northern, always on the starboard! That
southerners sailed with the wind on their left side and
"sail" grew slightly diagonally across their bladderlike l
from left to right. The northerners we picked up were ju
opposite.

In a deep-sea sailing ship there is plenty of time to
things and time to discuss them, too. We worked out a
genious theory that these jellyfish had evolved that desi

Those albatrosses used to be seasick as soon as they got aboard. When we let them go, they could not take off, though they ran along the surface a hundred yards and more and tried to get up and beat it with their great webbed feet. Once airborne they were magnificent, but there were at least some conditions in which they could do with assistance to get into the air.

It is reckoned that some two hundred thousand species of fish live in the sea, and between eight thousand and ten thousand species of plants thrive there. Down in the abyssal depths are the most extraordinary fish, voracious snapping monsters which creep about on stilts, cavernous mouths full of teeth like a tiger's, ready to rip into anything that comes along, including their own kind.

In those dark and impenetrable depths there are fish which carry their own flood-lighting systems or flashing lights on the end of long stalks growing from their heads, fish which get about on a sort of stilts to keep themselves above the deep, soft bottom ooze, fish of species in which the female carries around her husband on, or sometimes attached to, her own body—not because she likes him that much but to be sure he is there and not gone off to lose himself in the perpetual gloom. If he did, even she would have little chance of finding him again.

Fishing and ordinary seafaring are two different callings, not often mixed. Yet I have seen something of fishing both deep-sea and coastal—with the tuna traps off Faro at the entrance to the Mediterranean, with the Portuguese *barcos-do-mar* and sardine men, with a big trawler out of Grimsby in England fishing what they called the middle water grounds off the Faero Islands, and with the Portuguese Grand Banks dorymen in a modern steel four-masted schooner out of Lisbon to the Banks and Greenland—a six months' voyage.

The Grimsby trawler had a large bridge better equipped in

some ways than that of the Cunarder *Queen Mary*. No fish could come near the vessel, even fifty fathoms down, without throwing a white blob of light instantly on one or other of her electronic devices, called "fish loops." Electronic instruments of uncanny precision did all the navigation, took soundings continuously, and kept lookout. One especially marvelous instrument, coupled with a device for steering, could keep the trawler going down a defined lane with the exactitude of an expert driver on some maritime throughway, and keep a graphed record of everything it did as well. Loudspeakers blared the remarks—usually untruths about fish—of brother trawler skippers far and near.

To these our skipper paid acute attention. They might be lies, but he knew all those skippers' voices so well that he could detect how their ships were really doing, no matter what they said. With all their guile they could not keep slight but detectable changes out of their voices when they really were on fish in quantities. Some began to make jokes, some turned snarly; but they all gave themselves away. Our skipper guarded his secrets by saying nothing at all.

With all the instruments, fishing is still a very difficult business. A lot depends on the skipper's personal knowledge, acquired the hard way.

Trawlers cost a lot to build and to run. Their efficiency, in time, destroys the grounds they work over, not just the fish but what the fish live on and where they live. They might throw back small fish, but once in the trawl, the fish are dead or will soon die. Fish factory-ships keeping the sea for weeks and processing their catch in deep-freeze aboard, great fleets of ships such as the Russians use, take fish in ever increasing quantities—for a while. Then the banks give out, or the shelf is denuded; and the sea bed must mend again before fish may return in strength. The trawler can do nothing about that.

Alan Villiers

The Lisbon schooner *Argus* under way, bound for the fishing ground

But the Grand Banks doryman could. At least, his method of fishing does not spoil the sea bed at all, for he fishes with hook and line. The fish hook themselves; they are not mashed into a widemouthed remorseless net—massive and wirebound, hurtling along the sea bed swallowing or knocking down everything that comes in its way, fish mature and immature and all they live on.

Those Portuguese dorymen in the schooner *Argus*, and the others of the fleet of fifty large Grand Banks vessels, astonished me. Until I sailed with them in 1950, I did not know that so hard a life still existed. I was six months in the *Argus*. She had fifty-five dorymen, each fishing alone in a fragile, flat-bottomed,

wooden boat some fourteen feet by six. At dawn every morning the fifty-five dorymen went over the side and away, out of
sight of the schooner. They fished by paying out longlines with
anything from six hundred to a thousand hooks attached to the
longline on small lengths of line, called "snoods." They put
down these longlines skillfully across the tide and hauled in
the lot every four hours. They fished all day or until they had
filled their dory. Then they returned to the schooner and threw
their cod aboard.

They were huge cod—big fat fellows from rough, rocky
ground where the trawlers could not go, for the rocks would
have destroyed their gear. The *Argus* had to bring back seven
hundred tons of salted cod, cleaned and salted aboard. This
meant that the dorymen had to catch at least three thousand
tons of fresh fish, for fish when cleaned and salted shrink a lot.
We were six months. During all that time those calm, skillful
men cheerfully accepted the daily risk of being overwhelmed
in the sea, swept away in sudden storms, lost in fog, knocked
down by steamships (this was the open sea on the Atlantic
routes), even assault—unwitting—by whales.

A playful whale tipped one of our dorymen out, within sight
of the ship, fortunately. It was a nice whale and it stayed
around to see that he came to no permanent harm; but that
was cold water to be spilled into. We had another doryman
adrift for five days—lost, but found again. Several ships had
men drowned.

Those fifty-five Portuguese dorymen were the most courageous seafarers I have ever sailed with. Quiet, simple men,
some of them illiterate and all of them with a humble nobility,
one and all were skillful handlers of their little boats, great
fishermen, and prodigious workers. To be with such men was
a stimulating and indeed inspired experience in these troubled
times.

My *Argus* voyage was in 1950. In the mid-fifties I was back again, this time with the Portuguese hospital-assistance ship *Gil Eannes*. The Portuguese maintain a hospital ship for their four thousand dorymen and two thousand trawlermen on these distant banks. The unique four-thousand-ton motorship *Gil Eannes* has a sixty-bed hospital, a fully manned and equipped surgery, a fishermen's chapel and a priest, and a radio station to relay broadcasts to the dorymen from their families at home.

It was a stormy morning when, ten days from Lisbon via the Azores, the *Gil Eannes* sighted the first doryman. He was alone upon the sea, standing oil-skinned and sea-booted in the bows of his fantastic little boat, hauling in his longline. Over a little pulley in the bow the line came in, silvered with fat haddock, big halibut, long cod which he threw backward with a skillful flick of his wrists so they fell and stowed themselves in the boat—one flick for each. The dory was bucking like a bad-tempered bronco. It was raining. There was a nasty sighing moan in all the wind, and the sea looked cold, cheerless, malevolent and murderous. There was no sign of the schooner from which the dory had come. It was already noon; that doryman had been fishing an eight-hour day and would go on until nightfall, then clean and salt fish until all were stowed below. He had been out from home two months already and would be another four at least, perhaps five.

Of all the men in all the ships at sea that day in the whole North Atlantic, he and his kind were the *only* men braving the sea in tiny boats.

We passed close. The doryman turned for a moment toward us, and smiled and waved.

In the 1960's, only the Portuguese still fish by dory on the open Grand Banks and the arctic banks to the west of Greenland. French, Italian, Spanish, and Russian trawlers work there, some of them in vessels up to two thousand tons which, like the dorymen, salt their cod and often fish for six months. The Portuguese still use fifty dory-fishing vessels up to a thousand tons, twelve of them schooners. The big trawlers have to work farther and farther afield, switching from the Greenland banks to Bear Island, from off Iceland to off Norway, as fish may be found.

Something is being done at least to try to make up for the effects of overfishing—something, but not much. It is easier to destroy than to restore. In the United States, shad from the Atlantic have been reared successfully on the Sacramento River, in California, and a shad fishery established there. Russian scientists have successfully transplanted the Alaskan salmon to Europe and herring from the Baltic to the Aral Sea. By drenching a loch in Scotland with nutrient salts which immensely increased the growth of fish food there, Scotch marine biologists have shown that plaice so favored can put on two years' growth in six months.

In time, the sea's yield can be increased greatly, and the harm of overfishing can be overcome. There is scientific evidence that, acre for acre, the sea can be more productive than the land. *Can* be, yes—to make it so will take time and a good deal more knowledge both of fish and the ocean than we have today.

Chapter 14 • WHALES AND WHALING

THE LARGEST WHALE, THE BIG BLUE OF THE ANTARCTIC, IS the largest animal in the world. Very likely it is the largest animal there ever has been. One says animal, because whales are not fish but marine mammals—warm-blooded descendants of some large estuarial beast which, millions of years ago, took to the sea probably because the food was better there and perhaps also because it lacked means of defense. A big blue can weigh a hundred tons, be a hundred feet long; that is, it is much larger than many harbor tugs and weighs more than a mob of twenty-five full-grown elephants. But it cannot even bite. As for swallowing Jonah, its throat is so small that it is as much as one can do to shove a closed fist into it.

It was another sort of whale that swallowed Jonah. There are two principal types, which whalemen know as the whalebone and the toothed. The blue whale is chief of the whalebone type and the much smaller, barrel-headed sperm is chief of the toothed. Even he has teeth only in his snapping lower jaw, but they are teeth eight or nine inches long. The blue, the fin, the right, and the other whalebone whales, rather oddly, feed exclusively on the smallest creatures in the sea, stuff called plankton. They go to faraway places where these things abound—it takes tons of them to make a slight brown stain in the sea—and just swim along, big mouths open, gulping in plankton or *krill* by the ton. They have large soft tongues which look like balloons. They strain out the tiny creatures on the whiskered side of plates of whalebone (it isn't bone but soft stuff like a sort of pliable plastic) with which their upper jaws are lined. Then they expel the water and shove the little shrimps called *krill* back into their throats with their outsized tongues. They can go on doing this for months, during which they grow fat and sleek. Not only their blubber but their flesh and bones and everything become fabulously rich with edible oils.

Fin whales are smaller than blue and average about seventy-five feet in length. Both blues and fins frequent Antarctic seas in large numbers during the short summer months. Right whales are so called because whalemen once considered them the "right" whales to catch, mainly because of the quantities of long whalebone in their heads. This used to be very valuable when it was used for umbrella ribs, as framework for women's bustles and crinolines, and guardsmen's busbies. Right whales live mainly in the Arctic seas and used to be hunted north of Alaska by American sailing whaleships out of California ports, and in Greenland and Spitzbergen waters by Scots, Norwegians, and Dutchmen.

In the days of sailing whaleships and attacks on whales from open boats, the blue and fin whales were left strictly alone. It was not their bulk that saved them or their ferocious dispositions, for they are the quietest and most inoffensive creatures in the world. One thing only saved their lives. They sink when dead. Until fully mechanized whaling was possible, they *had* to be left alone.

Sperm whales float. They have the considerable convenience that their heads are literally big barrels of rich oil called spermaceti, which is valuable for candle-making and can be baled out. They are much smaller than blue whales, with an average length of about sixty feet. When prodded by harpoons and attacked with lances, they *can* be ferocious. They snap at whaleboats with their powerful lower jaws. They beat at men with their far more powerful tails, smash boats, drown men who get in the way. Some of them, lone old outcast bulls of morose and cunning disposition, learned from a successful encounter or two how to fight back at Yankee whalers in their fragile little boats. Some of these whales earned special names for themselves, like the notorious Mocha Dick, and were greatly respected. Mocha Dick killed many whalemen and was the real life counterpart of Herman Melville's Moby Dick. There was another notorious whale which deliberately rammed and sank the Nantucket whaler *Essex* in the Pacific, in 1820. Whaling captains, when they met at sea, used to exchange news of these notorious whales. They usually had old harpoons sticking in them and could be recognized and left alone.

The sperm is a most interesting whale, living largely on giant squid of a type never yet seen by men. Stories of enormous octopuses which were able to get their fifty-foot tentacles around medieval ships and take them under the sea are common in old sea lore. Old charts were often embellished with drawings of them, along with sea monsters and all sorts of things. Then, never having been seen, they were disbelieved in, even scoffed at. But the giant octopus does exist. He lives at great depths, far from the land.

Toward the end of 1962, I called at a whaling station near the port of Albany, in the southwestern corner of Australia. Around this corner, migrating sperm whales swing on a defined route into the Indian Ocean, spending some months on the way at the edge of the continental shelf, fighting and eating enormous squid. Whalemen told me there that they had seen a sperm break water, fifty or sixty miles out at sea, with an enormous octopus locked on his head. The octopus, they said, was flailing the whole body with tentacles all of fifty feet long and was trying to suffocate the whale by clinging over its nostrils.

Australian News and Information Bureau

Blubber is hoisted for cutting on the flensing deck of a shore station at Norwegian Bay, Western Australia.

Down would go the whale—down, down, down! The whalemen thought that the sperm fought back not only with his snapping jaws but by sounding with violent rapidity, flinging himself on the bottom, smashing and pulping the octopus' body, bashing it down with its barrel-head until it was forced to slip from the nostrils. Then the sperm rushed at once furiously for the surface, breaking with a great leap from the impetus of its mad rush bits of octopus still wound around it. Its lungs filled with air, it gorged on the pieces of octopus.

At the station, they had just finished dealing with half-a-dozen various-sized sperms. The stomachs of every one of them contained part-digested pieces of such enormous squid.

"What about pressure?" I asked, knowing that for us, as soon as we get below the surface of the sea, pressure increases by fifteen pounds per square inch of our bodies for each thirty-three feet we go down.

"Pressure doesn't bother the sperms at all," the whalemen said. "They can sound at great speed for half a mile. We know. We see our line run out."

Whaling was originally from beaches and rivermouths, then from land stations where the carcasses were brought in, hauled ashore, stripped of their blubber, and cut up for meat. Japanese were old hands at this sort of whaling, centuries ago. So were Basques, Eskimos, Faeroe Islanders, Norwegians, and Tasmanians. From this it was an easy step to the use of sailing ships which carried four or five slim, fast whaleboats at davits and were fitted with a simple boiling-down works on deck. An easy rig, usually that of a bark, minimal accommodation for the minimum number of mariners, a store of blubber-spades, knives, other essential gear, and a hold full of barrels completed the outfit.

Such blubber-hunters began soon to scour the seven seas. By the middle of the eighteenth century, there were hundreds of them sailing the Indian, Atlantic, and Pacific oceans. At the time of the American Revolution there were over seven hundred deep-sea Yankee whaleships at sea and over another hundred British ones.

Such ships did not just go off hopefully to sea and expect to find whales. Even then, they had considerable knowledge of the migratory movements of the sperm, humpback, and other types. They knew roughly where their main feeding-grounds were and when the whales visited them, when they might be found, say, on the New Zealand grounds, or around Hawaii, or the Maldive Islands in the Indian Ocean.

These old-time whalers made voyages which lasted for two or three years. Yankee crews often included islanders from the Azores, the Cape Verdes, the South Seas. They cruised on established grounds and lowered boats after whales, pulling up silently and planting their "irons" with courage and skill. There were exhilarating moments, dangerous moments, days and nights of prodigious toil and weeks of just sailing, with never a spout to be seen.

Often, frightened sperm whales, taking the harpoon like a bolting horse with the bit in its teeth, made off on the surface at a furious rate with the whaleboat towing behind like a great water ski gone mad, leaping, planing, almost flying, in a wild welter of spray and spume. Spilled-out men drowned. When at last the whale tired it could be killed only by means of a long, sharp lance. Boats had to get alongside for officers to use this lance, and the needled whale would often "flurry"—lash out most violently and dangerously in all directions.

It was a man's life and a strong man's, at that. To this day, tablets along the walls of churches in such whale ports as Nantucket and New Bedford bear their silent testimony to its dangers. Whale-hunters paid frequently with their lives.

There were compensations. Those wooden barks and ships were just about the most wonderful observation posts for studying surface sea life there ever were. They visited lovely, remote islands in the South Seas, discovered several of them and far too many reefs, sometimes remaining upon them as involuntary but very useful marks to warn their brother whalers. Men might turn beachcombers for a while, to taste the soft but heady delights of the languorous islands. Sometimes they had to become fighting men, to fight for their lives against islanders berserk from brutal exploitation and from treachery at the hands of callous and utterly brutal white men. For these also sailed among the islands, not in whalers.

Many whaleships established Yankee fortunes. One of them, the *Charles W. Morgan*—which is still to be seen in good state at Mystic Seaport on the Mystic River in Connecticut—earned $2 million over thirty-seven voyages during her whaling life. That 2 million would be worth 10 million now.

This sort of whaling came to an end through the exploitation of petroleum in the United States from 1860 onward, and the invention of the harpoon gun and the development of a mechanized whale-chaser to carry it. This Svend Foyn gun— named for its inventor—was a muzzle-loading cannon swinging freely on a pedestal in the bows of fast, swift-turning and very seaworthy little steamships, firing a nasty, grooved harpoon four feet in length and made of the best steel. This was pointed with a soft-iron bomb set by time fuse to explode in the whale's insides. The groove carries an attachment to which the fore-runner of the whale-line is made fast. A lookout barrel on the mast, a system of well-sprung blocks to take the shock of the thick harpoon line, a powerful winch like a trawler's to haul the dead whale to the surface when he sinks, and a nozzle to force air into the carcass to make it float complete the equipment.

Fitted out in this manner, with some tough Scot, Norwegian, Japanese, Dutchman, or Russian behind the gun, soon these little ships were working from land stations in the Arctic and Antarctic. Petroleum put spermaceti off the market as a means of illumination, but whale oil from the giant arctic and antarctic whales was still of value for prime soaps and oils and margarine.

First the steam-chasers worked from land stations. By 1902 the first of these in the Antarctic was established at the island of South Georgia and was immediately successful. From this it was an easy step to wholly pelagic whaling, to combining a modern whale factory-ship with a fleet of chasers which could scour the seas for whales wherever they were to be found.

Poor whales!

There was no mercy for them. The hunt became murder, the flensing and boiling-down a bloody butchery. Soon twenty-thousand-ton combination whale factory-ships and oil tankers were developed which, through giant ramps built into their fat sterns, could take even the largest blue whales aboard bodily. As the body moved along a disassembly line, men with sharp flensing knives and giant steam saws stripped off the blubber and ripped up the bones and flesh on working platforms as large as a ball park.

Such fleets could work in almost any weather, could handle fifteen hundred big whales in a short antarctic summer. With the further aid of whale-oil tankships to transport ten thousand tons or so of the oil halfway through the season, they could double their output—if the whales were there. Spotting aircraft, electronic underwater search, and radar were called in as aids. Steam pressure cookers and refined equipment were developed to waste nothing of the whale.

By the 1930's a score or so of these ruthlessly efficient giants were decimating the world's population of big whales at a rate never dreamed of—40,660 of them during the season 1938–1939 in the Antarctic alone, yielding almost 3 million barrels of oil.

The only way the poor whale could fight back was by showing such obvious signs of this overdone murder as refusing to grow to full size. But it was not really refusal—it was sheer inability. He did not get the chance. So obvious were the signs of decline in world whale stocks that the belligerents got together and formed a pact not to kill more than a mere sixteen thousand blue whales in a season. Sperms didn't count.

The difficulties of ice navigation in large steel ships and the shortness of the comparatively ice-free season are the only effective handicaps to the extinction of the whale, apart from such agreements. But there is an increasing awareness of the foolishness of so reducing whale stocks that the expensive pelagic factory-ships will no longer be profitable because of the scarcity of whales. After all, to operate at all, each of them has to find at least a thousand in a short season, and they have agreed not to take cows with calves or really immature whale. By 1963, they are really in trouble, for the whale stocks show alarming signs of running down.

I was once a member of the crew of one of these antarctic factory-ships—the very first, indeed, which went into the whales' last stronghold in the Ross Sea. Polar explorer Roald Amundsen had reported good whales to be there. The Norwegian whaler Carl Anton Larsen (who pioneered whaling from South Georgia), acting on this, raised some money, converted a tramp steamer of twelve thousand tons, bought five whale-chasers and headed for the Ross Sea in the summer of 1923, by way of Tasmania. I signed on there. I had not been to the Antarctic or had I been whaling, and it seemed an interesting thing to do.

It was—almost too much so.

The factory-ship—her name was the *Sir James Clark Ross*, after the discoverer of the Ross Sea—sailed from Hobart late in 1923, rolled and pitched her way through the roaring forties, the shrieking fifties, and the stormy sixties of south latitude. Taking the five chasers in tow, we then bashed a way through the pack-ice at the entrance of the Ross Sea. The old tramp had some greenheart protection on her bows, and that was all. Sometimes we were forced to a stop and all hands got out to bash at the ice with crowbars, or saw with long cross-cuts. This ice was unusually heavy and late. If a twelve-thousand-ton steamship had so much difficulty getting through it and took a week, I wondered, how about these whales we were after? How could a blubbery whale break through steel-like ice that stopped a strong ship?

Maybe the same thought occurred to our veteran commander, Captain Larsen. It certainly occurred to some pessimistic flensers and harpooneers we had aboard who were already regretting that they had not signed for their usual service with the South Georgia land station or one of the factory-ships anchored at the South Shetland Islands.

But we got through the ice at last, steamed to that wonderful sight, the Great Ice Barrier, a glacier-face of purest ice which stands at the end of the Pacific Ocean. It is not often one comes to the end of an ocean, but this was it, and unmistakably. The weather was appalling. Thick pack-ice spread all along the barrier face. Amundsen's harbor at the Bay of Whales was so full of pack as to be unusable.

And there were no whales, though the sea and the ice were stained tobacco-juice brown with billions and billions of *krill* waiting to provide a meal for them. It was savagely cold, even for the Norwegians, and howling blizzards shrieked down from that ice barrier without the slightest preliminary whistle of the wind. I had never had ice form in the corners of my eyes before.

When the whales came at last, they were enormous—averaging ninety feet and more, one of them 103 feet, long, white-freckled steely blue beauties which we in the factory-ship saw only on their backs, dead, with the ends of their large, horizontal flukes sheared off with a flensing knife. Even dead and turned over, they still had a grace of line as fine ships have. Deep corrugations extended from the points of their upturned

A good catch of blue whales round the *Sir James Clark Ross* in Discovery Inlet, Ross Sea

jaws back to their huge navels, perhaps to allow their stomachs to extend as they filled with tons of *krill*.

Not that these poor whales would ever need *krill* again. It seemed a terrible thing to take life from such mighty creatures.

We had taken their lives, but it was more difficult to take their blubber. The ship rolled and pitched too much. We could not get into the only harbors. When at last we did anchor in deep Discovery Inlet not far from the Bay of Whales, the place was a refrigerated nightmare. The dead whales froze up with the intense cold. Steam froze before it could get along to the deck winches. Flensers got frostbite. The inlet was far from sheltered; some of the ship's blubber-handling gear soon proved unsuitable.

But there were whales. Sometimes we could hear the booming of the harpoon guns as they were shot, two and three or more of those terrible harpoons to a whale. We knew how many bombs it took to kill them, for each dead whale carried notches cut into its tail—one for each harpoon, sometimes up to six.

"They sound deep—hundreds of fathoms. They rush up again. The yellow line sings out. The mast bends. They flurry madly! They blow blood! The sea turns all bloody! They sound. They rise. I fire another harpoon close in—this time without a line. . . . The flurry weakens. The blood spouts lower, thinner. They die silent, roll over on their backs, sink slowly into the bloodstained sea."

So a gunner-harpooneer described the killing which I saw too often myself, as the brief weeks of the icy summer dragged by.

"If the whale made any noise, even the smallest groan, I could not kill him," the gunner said.

His sympathy, too, was with the whales; but his living, like the ship's, depended on their slaughter.

Neither did very well out of that pioneering voyage of 1923–1924. But the whales were there, as Roald Amundsen had said they were. Modifications of her gear made the *Sir James Clark Ross* successful on her second voyage. From her, the slipway floating factories were developed; and soon the great whales in their last stronghold suffered man's onslaught on an unprecedented scale.

Poor whales! I saw one once in a huge tank near Los Angeles, a fat and friendly, nobbly-finned old fellow who learned to do tricks like the porpoises in another tank at the same place. He might even have learned to leap through hoops if one could have been contrived which was large enough for him, or had he room to leap and land again in the tank. There was a friendly, almost amused look in his eyes as if he were enjoying himself.

Then after a while, he died, too.

Chapter 15 • THE STUDY OF THE SEA

OCEANOGRAPHY IS THE SCIENCE OF STUDYING THE OCEAN IN all its aspects. Considering how important the ocean has been to man since life began, oceanography is astonishingly new. Benjamin Franklin took some interest in it about the time of the American Revolution. Another American, a naval officer named Matthew Fontaine Maury, published a book called *The Physical Geography of the Sea* in 1855, which is generally regarded as the foundation stone of modern oceanography.

Maury organized and collated information regarding wind and weather with particular application to better passage-making by sailing ships, as the German Hydrographic Office was also to do a little later. Maury's investigations led to better passages by ocean-going sailing ships whose masters had the sense to profit from them. Taking over the United States Hydrographic Office—then known as the Depot of Charts and Instruments and, until his time, regarded as just that—Maury did so thorough a job that to this day the United States pilot charts are still inscribed, "Founded on the researches of Matthew Fontaine Maury while serving as Lieutenant in the U.S.N."

This was one branch of oceanography. In 1872 the British commissioned the first ship to make a voyage concerned wholly with the study of the sea—not just the surface of the ocean, all of it. This was a tall order, and H.M.S. *Challenger* was almost four years on this pioneering voyage. She was a sailing ship without auxiliary power. When she stopped, she drifted. She

181

could take soundings only by the laborious process of stopping and lowering a weight on a rope, then heaving perhaps miles of the rope back aboard again. Yet she got soundings down to 4,475 fathoms in the Marianas trench in the Pacific. Her scientists had to use primitive nets to bring up their specimens from the depths. But they began the process of discovery of remarkable facts about the ocean and the ocean floor and laid down first principles in these and allied fields which still stand.

They found that the ocean bed is as varied as the surface of the land, with mountain ranges and deep valleys, plains and rifts and plateaus. They found its sea floor covered with all sorts of astonishing things, including dust from outer space which had fallen upon earth and sunk into the sea. For the first time, Sir John Murray was able, from the *Challenger's* observations, to prepare a chart of the bottom of the sea—not just a map with soundings, but a survey of the ocean floor and its bottom deposits.

Since the days of H.M.S. *Challenger*, many ships of several nationalities have made similar voyages, from the *Michael Sars* built by the Norwegian government in 1900, which carried out regular investigations in the North Atlantic for many years, to the British research ship *Discovery II* which began the same thing on a worldwide scale in the 1930's and in the 1960's is still on the endless job—from the big ketch *Atlantis* of the Wood's Hole Oceanographic Institute in Massachusetts, to the Russians' wonderfully equipped research ship *Vityaz*, the Danish *Dana* and *Galathea*, the chartered Swedish schooner *Albatross*, the American three-master *Vema*, and literally dozens more. There is work enough for all of them and a large fleet besides. The study of oceanography at sea costs a great deal of money. The work to date in the vast area of the world's tremendous oceans, thorough and painstaking as it has been, is comparable to the knowledge that would be acquired of a very large

Woods Hole Oceanographic Institution
The research ship *Atlantis*

lagoon, say, by a small flock of wading birds pecking at its rim and now and again flying over its surface and briefly landing.

Study is carried on also from many oceanographic institutes ashore, in Monaco, Britain, the United States, France, and elsewhere. Since the end of World War II this has been stepped up, but it was not until 1959 that the new science really came of age. In that year, some fifteen hundred scientists and research workers in various fields got together at the United Nations building in New York for the very first international Congress of Oceanography.

They had plenty to talk about. From the study of the migratory movements of labeled codfish in Arctic waters to the strange behavior of the Gulf Stream, from the astonishing mystery of the so-called "deep scattering layer" found by sound waves in the sea and understood by no one, to the many other puzzles being discovered in the marvelous world beneath the sea, the quest for knowledge picked up considerable momentum.

As for that "deep scattering layer"—why so-called I have no idea—this arose from the curious discovery of bounced-back sound waves in the depths of the sea where, as far as scientists are aware, there exists nothing to cause them to act that way at all. World War II saw rapid advances in the use of electronics at sea such as groping for submarines with instruments that gave out a telltale "ping-g-g-g, ping-g-g-g" and a compass bearing when their sound waves hit something; navigation buoys which signaled landing ships into the right beaches; radar which flashed a lighted chart on a dark surface as a weird instrument called a scanner swings around the top of a small mast, and so forth.

Sound waves could be made to do all sorts of things, at least in the way of providing data. But just what did this data always mean? For example, United States naval research on the trans-mission of sound waves turned up the extraordinary fact that in considerable areas of all oceans but the Arctic and Antarctic, a great cloud or mass or *something* gave back echoing vibrations always from a zone which was far from the sea floor, a sort of suspended echo-making cloud in watery space. Stranger still, its depth and area varied. It rose toward the surface by night and sank hundreds of fathoms by day. Sometimes there seemed to be several such "clouds" in the same area of the sea. Scientists still theorize as to what this could be. Perhaps it is an echo from myriads of the minute organisms called plankton which exist in the sea (but there are plenty of these in the cold seas too), or from shoals of deep-sea fish maybe, but what sort of fish? Not the slightest clue came up in any net.

It is well known that there is plenty of life in the sea, of course; but not even the researches of the most skillful sea divers like the French officer Jacques Cousteau could throw light on the problem. Underwater television has been tried. Marvelous diving boxes, little undersea ships called bathyscapes, have gone down and shone lights and searched exhaustively. They saw plenty, of course. The sea looked to observers in bathyscapes like a very thick soup that was squirming with bits of life; but nowhere was there any particular concentration of this stuff, no special layer of it, nothing to account for the extraordinary phenomenon of the bounced-back sound waves—nothing, apparently, that could bounce back anything.

But the bounce-back still goes on, with its steady diurnal fluctuation as reliable as the tides.

Another odd result of deep-sea investigations is the discovery that fish can "talk"—make sounds, anyway. It has been assumed that that clever and cheerful sea mammal, the porpoise, must have some sort of built-in natural radar system and can communicate somehow with its kind. But electronic instruments began to listen in on audible grunting, croaking, and groaning that could be made only by fish. Off Malaya and parts of the coast of China there is a fish known as the croaker which makes a distinctive noise. But these deep-sea fellows disturb the silence of the tropical depths in an astonishing manner. What they are making all the noise about nobody has yet discovered, though there is an optimist somewhere in the United States of America who is trying to learn to communicate with a well-trained and rather clever porpoise. If he does manage to do this he may learn a lot, but it is scarcely likely to be about the mysteries of really deep water.

All sorts of salts and minerals are held in solution in the sea, even small quantities of gold. Water can dissolve most things, at least in minute quantities. Water left in a glass will dissolve, in time, some scientifically measurable proportion of the glass. Sea water contains a host of mineral substances washed out of the earth's crust. In addition, there are organic salts derived from decaying plants and animals. Of all these extraneous items, approximately seventy-eight parts in each hundred is common salt, sodium chloride. Magnesium, calcium, potassium, and sulfate are also present in amounts exceeding one part per hundred. There are many so-called nutrients on which the prolific plant life depends. From one type of such plant alone, a certain kind of seaweed, a factory in the Outer Hebrides off Scotland produces a powdered substance from which commercial items as diversified as ice-cream base and soluble surgical dressings are later made. I have visited this factory, watched the powder cooking, seen the men bring in the harvest of long weed. Little steamships brought more from somewhere in the Shetland Islands.

This list of a few of the solvents in the sea indicates the difficulties of making pure water from sea water—difficulties now largely (though still expensively) overcome. The optimistic Dr. Bombard, crossing the Atlantic on his rubber raft *L'Hérétique*, claimed to have learned to drink sea water—a practice heavily discouraged by all seamen (though a Chinaman from a torpedoed Blue Funnel liner survived for 130 days on a raft during World War II, and nobody knows what he drank for all that time, or lived on).

It is very expensive to condense fresh water from the sea, although many large steamships now do so. In 1962, a claim was made for a new process developed by the General Electric Company which, it was said, could produce forty-two pounds of fresh water from each hundred pounds of sea water treated, without boiling the water at all and using about a fourth of the energy necessary in other systems. If this is so, it is a considerable step ahead. Fresh water is short in many parts of the world, sometimes becoming alarmingly so, and sea water must be used increasingly to overcome shortages.

However deep man has been able to get down in the sea with trawl or net or coring instrument, he has not yet reached to the end of its life. A trawl brought up by the Soviet ship *Vityaz* from 5,858 fathoms in the western Pacific showed an astonishing benthos population. Cores taken from the deepest part of the oceans show traces of life. Net hauls down to fifteen hundred fathoms have brought up extraordinary collections of fishes and crustaceans all adapted to live in that frigid, unlit, and highly pressurized world.

There is no depth yet reached where life of some kind has not been discovered, even if only sluggish salpa or baleful benthos. When Dr. Beebe went down half a mile in his bathysphere—a very strongly built steel sphere with specially designed lookout windows made of quartz—he reported seeing many kinds of fishes which have not yet been brought to the surface. Some of these had enormous mouths with loosely fixed jaws so that, whatever came along, they could work their mouths around it and dispatch it at leisure with their scimitar-sharp teeth—so long as it didn't dispatch them first.

The study of the sea has received a great fillip in recent years. New instruments can do wonderful things, such as accurately recording wave heights and tide or current movements from a ship going through the water at speed. A device known, for some reason, as a bathythermograph, makes an accurate and continuous record of undersea temperatures while a ship above it steams along. Its companion instrument, a geomagnetic electro-kinetograph, does the same thing for variations in the water movements and so is invaluable for storing up data for accurately assessing ocean currents. Instantaneous echo-sounding makes a precise record of ocean depths. Wave-measurers replace guess-work (but not yet entirely). Sea water samples are taken at depth by an ingenious system of bottles strung upside down on fine wire and manipulated as required by "messenger," which flips each over in turn at the proper depth, allows them to fill, then insulates the sample against pollution as it is hauled up. As one sample bottle is filled the messenger descends and turns the next. Self-recording thermometers retain a reading of the temperature at which the sample was taken.

More wonderful devices establish such things as the varying viscosity in the sea (the internal friction of the water particles), which has been noted as being twice as marked at temperatures of 41° F. as at 77° F. An odd fact like this, on further investigation, reveals that minute planktonic animals can hang suspended in colder water with much less effort than in warmer water. Some have been observed to sprout feathery attachments to their bodies in order to increase their buoyancy in the warm water.

Who cares, you might ask, if a pinhead plankton in the depths of the sea grows "feathers" to reduce the effort of remaining in the same place? What an odd piece of information to send expensive ships and scientists to sea and to spend so much time and money to find out!

But man is just beginning the real study of the ocean which so greatly affects his daily life. As the world becomes more crowded and food and even fresh water become scarcer for so high a proportion of the earth's population, man must look to the sea for aid. It will not help him much if he does not quite know what he is looking for, or at. Every smallest item of fresh knowledge, no matter how expensively or painstakingly acquired, may be invaluable.

Already, French engineers have been able to produce power

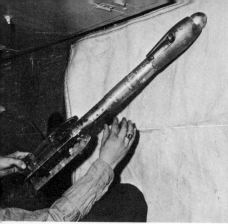

U. S. Naval Oceanographic Office

Two of the instruments used by oceanographers—left: a smoked slide is inserted into a bathythermograph; right: retrieving a nansen bottle from a cable with a high wire angle.

from the temperature differences between surface and near-bottom water, which they have induced to drive experimental turbines—and this is only one among the tremendous list of the extraordinary, diverse, and profitable resources which, when he finds out how, man may draw from the sea.

So there it is, in brief summary, some outline, and a few details, the vast and endless story of man and the ocean, *his* ocean if he can make it so. The great sea highway is now raced across by eighty-thousand-ton liners with antiroll stabilizers for the comfort of their passengers and for minimizing the rate of crockery loss, and by tankers even larger, operating with an unprecedented efficiency, each carrying in its colossal tanks more oil than previously was transported in a fleet. Other tankers can give rapid bulk transport to materials never moved in this way before, from hot asphalt to cold orange juice, liquefied gas to Californian wine.

Behind ships in the North Atlantic trade stands a unique weather information service based on an international fleet of special ships stationed in such a way as to cover the whole storm-breeding area of that frequently wild ocean. Every iceberg which lumbers down the Labrador current or is spilled out of the Greenland stream is plotted from the sea and from the air, and its whereabouts broadcast to shipping. Incipient hurricanes are noted, watched, tracked, and reported as they develop, that ships may avoid their greatest force. Salvage tugs are based strategically to rescue and tow lame ducks in from sea. Every port and harbor that ships use, every headland they pass, every danger in the sea, is well charted, marked, and lighted in an unmistakable manner publicized internationally and known to seamen. International regulation insures that ships do not go to sea overloaded, undermanned, or unseaworthy in any way.

Beneath the sea, nuclear-powered submarines dash around the earth or slip carelessly beneath the arctic ice by a new version of the Northwest Passage, from the Pacific to the Atlantic, without having once to surface or refuel. Twenty-knot cargo-liners deliver the freights of the world on schedule. Hydrofoil craft, lifting themselves on twin hydrofoils like gigantic water skis, race passengers through Norwegian fiords, on the Rhine, from Capri to Naples, on Lake Constance, on the Volga and across the Strait of Messina between Sicily and Italy, with what used to be regarded as the speed of aircraft. Big saucer-shaped sea vehicles called hovercraft ride swiftly on short runs supported on cushions of compressed air of their own making, and already these operate some British ferry services. In the United States, even faster craft called water gliders are designed to operate on a similar principle and to go even faster.

By the 1970's, cheap nuclear power for merchant ships may be a commonplace and submarine tankships able to carry one hundred thousand tons of oil will be moving below the ice to carry away oil from Canada's arctic fields. Submarine freighters up to five thousand tons operated in World War II, but these were designed to make long voyages mainly on the surface, diving only when compelled. The new submarines are to take advantage of the quiet water below the surface even in the wildest storm. They are intended to operate at depths of one hundred to three hundred feet and only to come to the surface in ports. The advantages of such underwater freighters have been appreciated by shipping men for a long time, but, to make them worthwhile, economic nuclear propulsion must first become available. This is expected to arrive soon.

On the sea and under the sea, above the sea and around the sea, progressive man speeds on.

He still can spare some time and energy for adventure on the sea, as well. The prodigious increase in the sport of yachting both coastal and on the oceans is evidence of this. More yachts are sailed by more people to more places today than ever before. At any one time, twenty or thirty of them are wandering the Pacific alone, and ten or twelve others are tied up in Tahiti. While the great sailing ship has disappeared from the ocean routes, yachts race across the North Atlantic, beat through the Strait of Magellan, run like midget Magellans before the Pacific and Indian Ocean trades, race by the score to distant offshore islands.

At last, too, man is really trying to understand his sea-girt world, and to give due consideration to the lives also of all those infinite species which, in their varied but always interesting ways, share its wealth and mysteries with him.

BIBLIOGRAPHY

THE INTERESTED STUDENT MAY FIND MANY BOOKS TO GAIN FURTHER knowledge of the sea, its story, and its inhabitants. For easy reading, perhaps the *Science of the Sea,* by G. H. Fowler and E. J. Allen (1928), Sir Alister Hardy's *The Open Sea, the World of Plankton* (1957), and the second volume, *Fish and Fisheries* (1959), Sir John Murray and Johan Hjort's *The Depths of the Ocean* (1912), F. S. Russell and C. M. Yonge's *The Seas: Our Knowledge of Life in the Sea, and How It Is Gained* (1944) may be recommended, with Rachel L. Carson's well-known *The Sea Around Us* (1951) and Dr. F. D. Ommanney's various works, particularly *The Ocean* (1961).

For old-time whaling Frank Bullen's *Cruise of the Cachalot* (1895) is still the classic; Melville's *Moby Dick* is also of value. For modern whaling the best books are in Norwegian, but there is at least one good book in English, A. G. Bennett's *Whaling in the Antarctic* (1932).

For the voyages of discovery, there are Dr. J. C. Beaglehole's *The Exploration of the Pacific* (1934), Professor Prestage's *The Portuguese Pioneers,* and Dr. J. A. Williamson's *Cook and the Opening of the Pacific.* Rear-Admiral S. E. Morison's *Admiral of the Ocean Sea* (1942) deals fully with Columbus.

For life in Arab dhows, my *Sons of Sinbad* (1940) is the only modern narrative. *A Short History of the World's Shipping Industry* by C. E. Fayle (1933) is an excellent work, and easy to follow.

There is a series on the separate oceans—the *Indian, Pacific, Coral Sea, Atlantic* (called *The Western Ocean* in London, *Wild Ocean* in the United States), *Mediterranean,* and *Antarctic*—published by Museum Press in London and McGraw-Hill in New York.

To keep up with developments at sea the young general reader can hardly do better than to read the *National Geographic* Magazine, published by the National Geographic Society of Washington, D.C., which reports on any outstanding achievement.

192